SUSPENSION — STEERING — SPRINGS & SHOCKS

CHASSIS TUNING

By Jan P. Norbye

New York
SPORTS CAR PRESS

©1972 by Sports Car Press, Ltd.
Published in New York by Sports Car Press Ltd.
and simultaneously in Ontario, Canada by
General Publishing Co.
Produced by Silvermine Production, Norwalk, Conn. 06850

Library of Congress Catalog Number 72-83690
ISBN 0-87112-058-5

Contents

FOREWORD

Chassis tuning is becoming more and more important to the car owners of America, as the emphasis is taken off engine tuning by federal emission control laws. While it is true that the auto industry is improving its chassis engineering at an accelerated pace, it's also true that standard equipment on a mass-produced car, domestic or imported, hardly comes up to the full road-holding potential of the basic chassis.

There are many ways to achieve such improvements on nearly every car, but the way to begin is not by practical experiment but by acquiring a thorough understanding of cause and effect in suspension design and modifications. The next thing to do is to fix in mind the cautionary note that a modification which has worked to advantage on one car will not necessarily have the same effect on another.

There are also a few people across the country who build their own "specials" in home workshops and garages, using varying proportions of stock suspension parts. For them, the above statements are even more important.

The enthusiastic owner-driver is discouraged, however, from changing the basic suspension on his car, because fundamental changes are always expensive and there is always an experimental element in their character.

But there are several fields where relatively inexpensive alterations can literally transform the handling characteristics of a vehicle, and I am going to explain them in detail after the basic principles have been established. The purpose of chassis tuning is to achieve improvements in ride and handling.

What is meant by ride and handling? "Ride" is essentially concerned with ride comfort, or the cushioning of road shocks, and the elimination of road noise, vibration and harshness.

"Handling" is a somewhat more complex idea. Perhaps it's easier to grasp if we start off by saying what is is *not*. It's not the ease of backing into a tight parking spot. It's not the ease with which the steering wheel can be turned. Once those two basic facts are firmly grasped, it becomes almost simple.

Handling is concerned with vehicle control at speed, or the way cars respond to driver commands in terms of directional control. That means the ease and precision with which it is possible to change the vehicle's course into any new desired path, and to maintain this new path, or make further changes in the path or heading.

That's handling, as seen from the driver's viewpoint. If the car had a viewpoint, it would be its roll, pitch and yaw motions as produced either by driver-applied steering inputs, or by outside disturbances in the form of roadway unevenness or sidewinds.

The roll, pitch and yaw motions of the car are determined by a number of different factors included in the chassis design. These factors are called interacting design parameters, and we'll study them all in some depth later on. The point I want to make right now is that they are interdependent. Change one, and several others will automatically undergo a certain change as well. Conversely, a change in one may dictate changes in others so as to counteract undesirable side effects. Suspension and chassis engineers know what they are, and can build the exact handling characteristics they want into a car. Then why aren't all cars built with impeccable handling?

The problem is that certain design parameters are locked in when the decision to make a certain type of car is taken. For instance, an eight-seat station wagon cannot have the same handling potential as a two-seat roadster. Why? You'll see as we go along.

As an extra complication, there is some disagreement among the experts as to just what combination of handling characteristics is the most desirable.

Each team of chassis engineers choose the control and stability characteristics of the car they are designing on the basis of the desired ease of maneuvering and course-keeping at speed.

Most experts agree that high steering precision and high stability in cornering are desirable. Both of these qualities are implied when you say "good steering response". In other words: If the steering response is quick enough, yet free from overshoot, a certain steering input will change the vehicle's course from whatever it is to a newly selected path, straight or curved, in stable and unhesitating fashion. There's much more to obtaining this than stearing gear ratio, linkage, and turning circle. It involves basic chassis design and chassis tuning.

Chassis tuning is not so much correcting the "errors" built into the car at the factory, as adapting your car to the exact handling characteristics which you, the owner and driver, prefer.

This book regards the field of chassis tuning from your point of view. It may help you select your next car, but above all, it is written with your present car in mind, and will try to explain what you can do in order to get better satisfaction in the areas of ride and handling.

You may be surprised at how much you can do with a limited budget. This goes for domestic as well as for imported cars.

This book is concerned mainly with steering and suspension systems. It is not proposed to go into frame structures or even brakes, which are part of chassis engineering, but do not really belong in a study of chassis tuning for improved ride and handling.

Conventional chassis design is typified by the 1970 Ford Torino.

THE AUTOMOBILE CHASSIS

Definitions

There's a world of difference between turning the steering wheel and making the car turn. The steering wheel just sets up a certain steer angle in the front wheels, and they don't necessarily go where they are pointed. Different cars respond differently to the same steering wheel input. Now, before we go deeper into it, it would seem proper to give a few definitions so as to avoid needless misunderstanding and confusion.

Steering Gain
When a small steering wheel input makes the car turn sharply, the car has high steering gain. Many people often call this "quick response" but to suspension engineers, gain and response are two different things. Gain is the amount of turning produced in the complete car by a given steering wheel input.

Response
Response is the time it takes the car to go from one steady-state condition to another, or the time it takes for the car to change its direction and settle into a stable condition on a new course. Cars with high response have high gain and tend to straighten out without delay. Cars with low response have low gain, and are slow to line up on the new course. Countersteering may become necessary, as slow response often involves overshoot.

Road Feel
The technically correct term for road feel is *feedback*. Feedback is information about moment-to-moment conditions at the front tire footprints, delivered to the driver via the steering wheel. Such infor-

mation helps the driver make the decisions he must make continuously to keep the car on the intended path. Feedback is a measure of the self-aligning torque generated at the front tire footprints. It varies in strength according to the friction coefficient between the tire footprint and the road surface, and with the slip angle of the tires. This feedback tells the driver how much of the car's cornering ability he is making use of; it enables the driver to feel slipperiness in the road surface, and to detect an incipient skid in time to make steering corrections and remain in control.

Roll, Pitch and Yaw

These are the freedoms of motion in the car. Roll can be described as leaning to one side (tilt) with all four wheels on the ground. It means compressing the springs on one side and stretching the springs on the other side.

Pitch is a nodding action in the car, compressing the front springs and unloading the rear ones, and vice versa, usually in a cyclical pattern.

Yaw means the same in a car as it does in a yacht or an airplane. It means a sideways turn of the entire vehicle. Any of these motions can occur single or in any combination with one or both of the others.

Roll, pitch and bounce are kept to a minimum in order to obtain the best possible ride comfort. Roll is caused by side forces, such as centrifugal force on a curve. Pitching is caused by fore-and-aft load transfer, and can be controlled but not totally eliminated. Yawing motions are necessary for the directional control of the car.

Cornering Ability

By cornering ability we mean a car's ability to follow a curved path under a certain lateral force with full retention of traction and directional control. How does traction get into this? Because if a car is make to turn so sharply that one of its driving wheels is lifted off the ground, traction is lost.

Directional Stability

By directional stability we mean a car's ability to travel straight ahead without reacting to extraneous forces, such as bumps or undulations in the road surface, or aerodynamic disturbances such as sidewinds.

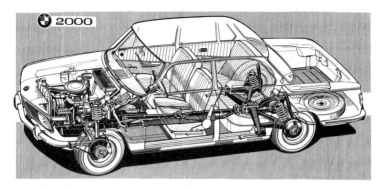
BMW 2000 is a good example of modern chassis design.

Understeer and Oversteer

Understeer means that the vehicle resists any deviation from a straight path. It tends to go straight. It has high directional stability and low but steady response. *Oversteer* means that the vehicle tends to exaggerate the steering command given by the driver. Steering gain rises at a higher rate than the steering angle. An oversteering car has poor directional stability and unpredictable response.

If a car understeers, the path radius for a given steering angle will increase as the speed increases. Oversteer tends to diminish the radius with increasing speed.

It's important to understand that understeer and oversteer refer to momentary transient conditions as well as the basic handling characteristics of a car. All cars have some initial understeer, because the front tires need time to build up side-bite. It's also possible for a car that normally understeers to be put into an oversteering condition—but the stronger the basic understeer, the more difficult it is to provoke oversteer. And a car that understeers slightly at low lateral accelerations (low side forces) will often oversteer at high lateral accelerations. There are a number of things you can do to add to or reduce understeer. The details are given in a later chapter.

Weight Distribution

Weight is not distributed evenly throughout the chassis. It is important to keep track of weight concentrations since they dictate both the location of the center of gravity and the polar moment of inertia. Both of these have enormous influence on a car's handling charac-

Suspension geometry changes radically during severe cornering.

teristics. In return, suspensions design has enormous influence on weight transfer.

The center of gravity matters in more than one plane. Its vertical position is of vital importance, but its place in the fore-and-aft plane also has a bearing on the car's handling characteristics.

Just how far forward or backward, in relation to the front and rear wheels, the center of gravity is located, sets the stage for a certain kind of behavior. That's because centrifugal force acts through the center of gravity. Engineers don't agree just where it should be, though. All they agree on is that if it's too far forward, centrifugal force will tend to counteract and minimize any directional change input from the steering wheel. And if it's too far backwards, centrifugal force will tend to produce directional instability, culminating at the point where all directional control is lost. This is an oversimplification, but nose-heavy cars tend to understeer, and tail-heavy cars tend to oversteer.

The total vehicle weight is divided into sprung and unsprung weight masses. The wheels and tires are unsprung weight. The front wheel spindles and spindle support arms are unsprung weight. The tie rods and suspension control arms are partially unsprung weight. The front springs are partially unsprung weight. The rear axle is unsprung weight and its locating arms are partially unsprung weight. The rear springs are partially unsprung weight, and the propeller shaft is partially unsprung. All parts that move up and down on deflection of a road wheel contribute to the unsprung weight. The frame and body, engine and transmission, and all other parts are sprung weight. The sprung-to-unsprung weight ratio should be as high as possible for the best combination of ride and handling.

In other words, the less unsprung weight the better, but especially in a light car. Weight transfer will be discussed after we have looked at suspension systems and roll centers.

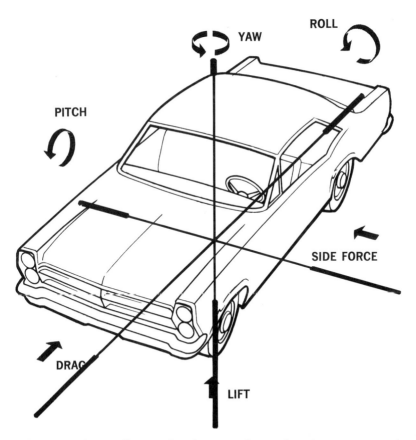

System of coordinates for the car shows freedom to move in three planes

Polar Moment of Inertia

The polar moment of inertia is an indication of the car's readiness to change its direction of travel. Inertia is the force that a body has at its disposal to resist any change in velocity. Let's put it this way: a body at rest will remain at rest until disturbed by an outside force. It logically follows that a body travelling in a straight line will continue in a straight line until deflected by an outside force. Moment of inertia is a measure of the resistance in a certain body. Polar moment of inertia is a measure of the resistance to turn a body about a certain axis.

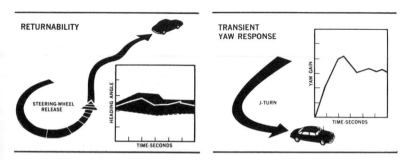

Left, returnability is tested by sudden steering wheel release on a sharp turn and clocking time elapsed before vehicle regains steady state. Right, transient yaw response is tested by clocking time from start of turn to its completion.

If the body in question is a car, it doesn't matter if the outside force is a change in road camber, a gust of sidewind, or a steering command from the driver. But in a car, response to the third is desirable, while response to the second is undesirable, and response to the first is just about inevitable.

It's the location of the masses in the chassis that determine the polar moment of inertia. Think of each mass as a pole of inertia. Taken all together, they dictate the location of the center of gravity. And the center of gravity may be far removed from any of the main inertia poles, and this is the key to understanding why the polar moment of inertia is so important.

Now we have to introduce the yaw axis, which is the center for all the car's yaw motions. The yaw axis usually doesn't stray too far from the center of gravity, but the two do not necessarily coincide.

Double lane change tests initial response and gain plus two steering reversals against the stopwatch.

You can calculate the polar moment of inertia if you know the weight of each mass and the distance between its center of gravity and the car's yaw axis.

The higher the weight and the longer the distance, the higher the polar moment of inertia. A chassis with its masses heavy and far apart has the highest polar moment of inertia. When they are light and close to the middle of the chassis, the polar moment of inertia is low.

Sports cars with front engines set well back in the chassis and very little rear overhang have a low polar moment of inertia. Rear-engined cars have a high polar moment of inertia, with the effective mass in the tail rather than in the nose. Cars with midships engines have a low polar moment of inertia; this configuration is prominent on racing cars, where payload requirements are nonexistent.

A car with a high polar moment of inertia tends to resist turning. A car with a low polar moment of inertia turns easily. This can be explained by thinking of a dumbbell. It is a straight bar with a weight at each end. When grasped in the middle and twisted, it resists the twisting motion. If one weight had been placed in the middle of a straight bar, with no weights on the ends, a hand holding the central weight could twist the bar practically without resistance.

21

The inertia of the engine mass and the tank-and-tire mass resist any force that tends to move them, just as the inertia of the weights on the dumbbell resist all twisting forces on the bar.

Understeer and Oversteer

Understeer and oversteer are basic expressions of a car's cornering ability. You probably have some idea why certain cars oversteer and others understeer. If the Volkswagen oversteers, you may conclude it's because of the rear engine. You may think it's the combination of an engine overhanging the rear wheel center line with a system of independent suspension known as "swing axles". You're on the right track.

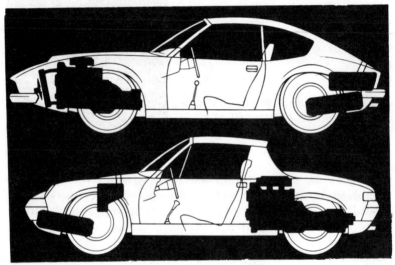

Front wheel drive car (on top) has high polar moment of inertia, while midships-engined car (below) has low polar moment of inertia.

If a Thunderbird understeers, you are likely to conclude that the heavy engine up there in the nose of the car, combined with the soft front springs, has something to do with it. No doubt. There are many other factors that affect the car's steer characteristic. They will be explained in the next chapter. Here I merely want to discuss the advantages of moderate understeer.

Some amount of understeer is desirable. The driver can afford to take his eyes off the road for a moment without risking that the car will change direction before he looks again. He can bring the car smoothly into a curved path and achieve a state of balance in that path without difficulty. He can leave the original curved path and take a different one, with shorter or longer radius, or return to a straight-ahead course with the car in complete balance.

An understeering car is directionally stable because the centrifugal force acting at the car's center of gravity will tend to counteract and minimize the directional change.

If an understeering car is headed into a curve of a given radius at

Dumbbell has high polar moment of inertia, while single ball at turn center has low polar moment of inertia.

excessive speed, the front wheels will reach a point where they cease to have any steering effect and begin to drift to the outside of the curve. If the car has enough power to spin the rear wheels, the driver can regain directional control by standing hard on the throttle and thereby breaking the rear wheels loose—this will force the tail towards the outside of the turn and point the car back on its intended course.

Naturally, this is an extreme maneuver which takes a highly expert driver. What it consists of is, to provoke more than enough oversteer to counteract the understeer that is threatening disaster, and thereby produce a near-neutral steering condition. In this situation, the front wheels will regain their grip, and the skilled driver will find his control restored. The recommended way for the less proficient conforms to the natural reactions of the inexperienced:

When the front wheels of an understeering car begin to drift, merely backing off on the accelerator can bring the speed down to a level that enables the front wheels to regain their sidebite by themselves.

In many understeering cars, the brakes can be applied for the same purpose without danger.

An oversteering car is unstable because the effect of a side load will be magnified by the centrifugal force. Centrifugal force increases with the square of car speed and for any given oversteering car a critical speed will exist. At this critical speed, even the smallest additional side load will result in a spinout unless the driver takes extremely quick corrective action. The same instability that makes oversteer undesirable on the straightaway enables an oversteering car to get around sharp turns faster than an understeering car. But it takes a highly expert driver to manage an oversteering car.

Makers of inherently oversteering cars disguise their oversteering characteristics by specifying low front tire pressures to increase front slip angles, and by increasing front wheel caster angles in order to increase directional stability. No cars are made with *neutral steer.* If a neutral steering car were made, it would tend to switch back and forth between understeer and oversteer as it encountered changes in the loading and driving conditions. This would result in a confusing control situation for the driver.

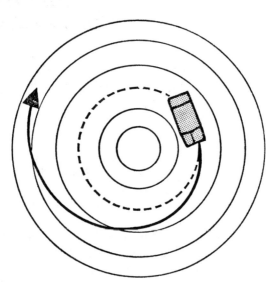

Speeding up understeering car from base circle (dotted line) while holding steering wheel still results in car going wide.

Modern front-engine, rear-drive cars with mild understeer at low speed and under light side force tend toward neutral steer at high speeds and/or high side forces. This is true of several small and medium-size European sedans as well as some full-size American cars with superior road manners. It has been achieved by tailoring the suspension geometry, spring deflection, roll stiffness distribution and tire properties to the weight distribution and overall dimensions of the vehicle.

Optimum stability will be obtained if the car's center of gravity coincides with the neutral steer line. The neutral steer line is a point on the car's center line, positioned where no side force acting on it can produce any yaw angle in the car. That's why it's called the neutral steer angle.

The car would be pushed sideways but would still be pointing in the same direction. In other words, centrifugal force would be evenly distributed to front and rear wheels. Directionally, the car would be in complete balance.

If the center of gravity is located ahead of the neutral steer line, the

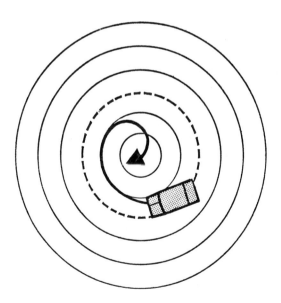

Speeding up oversteering car from base circle (dotted line) without changing steering wheel position results in spinout.

car will tend to understeer. If the center of gravity is located behind the neutral steer line, the car will tend to oversteer.

Front Wheel Drive

Front wheel drive has made great gains in popularity in the last decade, especially in smaller cars, though Oldsmobile and Cadillac have demonstrated its feasibility in very large and heavy vehicles. Front wheel drive offers many advantages. First, traction. With front wheel drive and rear-engined cars, the engine mass puts extra load on the driving wheels. More weight means better traction. Conventional cars do not have this advantage.

Traction is more important at low speed than at high speed. At high speed, there is plenty of dynamic energy stored in the vehicle. At low speed, traction must overcome the inertia of the vehicle mass in order to accelerate it. From the point of view of straight-line traction, front drive comes off best under most conditions. With the driver alone on board, the rear-engine, rear-drive car cannot challenge the front-drive car on level ground, uphill or downhill, With a full complement of passengers and luggage, the rear-drive car has superior traction on an uphill gradient, but the front drive car still has better traction on the level and downhill. The wheels that drive a front drive car always point in the same direction it is steered.

Inertia in the vehicle itself will cause understeer and a difference in steering angle and direction of travel, but traction is always applied in the direction the front wheels are pointed. Since the car is never in any doubt about which direction it is headed, its structure can be lighter. The need for reinforcements will be smaller.

Next, directional stability. The average front drive car has superior directional stability to the average rear drive car because of its inherent self-centering tendency. This tendency is effective at all speeds. A nose-heavy front drive car is inherently understeering. However, it is less understeering at high speed than at low speed.

The kind of understeer that comes with front drive is a manageable kind of understeer. It always moderates the curve path if the driver makes a sudden steering wheel movement, or accelerates or brakes too hard for the curve indicated by the steering angle. Such features may not give optimum maneuverability but give most drivers a feel-

Engine position and drive train configuration has major effect on weight distribution.

ing of being at ease when driving such a car. With front drive, front wheel breakaway is a stable motion with a self-diminishing tenency. This means added safety in an emergency situation.

When entering a turn at excessive speed, because the driver overestimated the adhesion of the road surface, the front drive car risks floating out at the front end. This is called extreme understeer. Backing off on the throttle will enable the driver to regain a shorter turn radius. The car will slow down and the driver will retain control.

In an examination of space utilization, the front drive car comes off best. It has a spacious trunk in the tail of the car, made roomier because there is no need for a rear axle with lots of free space to bounce

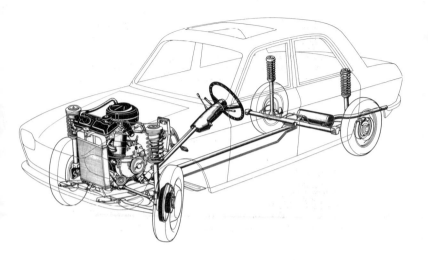

Peugeot 204 has transverse engine and front wheel drive.

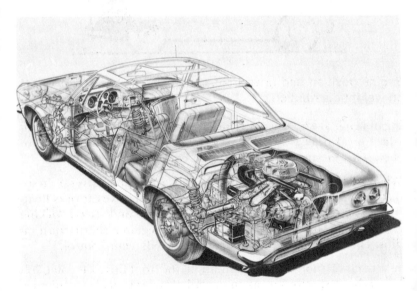

Chevrolet Corvair had rear engine and rear wheel drive.

around in. The front drive car also has a flat floor, since all drive train components and their control organs are up front. That means a low center of gravity and reduced risk of rollover.

A low center of gravity gives good ride characteristics because carrying the load of occupants and luggage closer to the ground means smaller side movements in the vehicle when crossing asymetrically applied bumps. It also permits a lower roll center without excessive risk of body roll on curves. Passenger comfort is best in a front-drive car, because all drive train vibrations can be kept in the nose of the car.

Rear Engined Cars

By rear engines is meant engines overhanging the rear wheel axis, i.e., carried in the tail of the car, outside the wheelbase. This type of chassis design has advantages in several areas. With the engine mass above the driving wheels, traction is almost as good as with front wheel drive. With the engine weight removed from the front end, the steering effort is reduced (and a lower steering gear ratio may be used). But the rear engined car cannot have a flat floor, even if the propeller shaft is eliminated, because of the need for connections between hand and foot controls up front and the engine and transmission in the back. Rear-engined cars have small trunks (in front) because the wheels need space to steer.

But the worst drawback in rear engined cars is the weight distribution. Many such cars tend to oversteer, and most have poor directional stability.

Mid-Engined Cars

With the engine mounted centrally in the chassis, just ahead of the rear wheel axis, the situation is radically different from rear engine

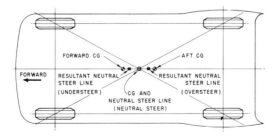

Center of gravity location has an important effect on the neutral steer line.

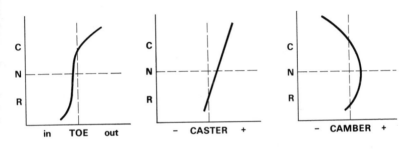

Caster, camber and toe-in change during spring deflections
C=compression; R=Rebound; N=Normal

chassis design. Mid-engined cars have the same traction advantages with none of the weight distribution problems.

They have the same lightness of steering, and the same lack of luggage space. But the main problem about mid-engine chassis design is the difficulty of a back seat installation. The designer has the choice of stretching the chassis to accommodate both engine and back seat at normal levels, or raising the rear seat (and roofline) to clear the engine housing. In both cases, there is a problem of heat insulation for the back seat. And neither case is an ideal solution, so the mid-engine chassis is pretty well restricted to two-seater sports cars and various types of racing machinery.

THE SUSPENSION SYSTEM
Suspension Principles

The first duty of the suspension system is to hold the wheels on the car. The suspension system in this context is made up of control linkages, and the springs do not enter the picture except when they do double duty as locating members.

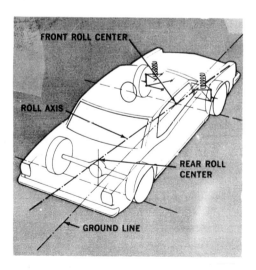

Height of front and rear roll centers determining the roll axis.

These suspension linkages must be tremendously strong, for they must transmit enormous loads. The highest loads are experienced in braking. For an illustration of this, say a 250-hp car can accelerate from zero to 60 mph in 12 seconds. It can stop from 60 mph in 4 seconds, which means the brakes performed 750 hp worth of work. Since two-thirds of the braking is done by the front wheels, that means the front suspension linkage withstood the thrust of 500 hp and transmitted the load into the frame and body structure.

The suspension linkage for the driving wheels must take torque, thrust and torque reactions into account. The loads are lower, but wheel movement must be controlled. The control arms are also subject to lateral loads, and must be designed to withstand all stress loads without bending or cracking. Suspension geometry is designed for front and rear wheels to control wheel positions as they follow the road surface, through bumps, potholes, across grooves and ridges, tar strips and waves.

When the car is at standstill the wheels seem vertical and aimed straight ahead. That's not quite so, as we shall see in the chapter on steering, but it's accurate enough in this connection. The point to be made here is that the wheels undergo wide changes in camber, caster and toe-out during up-and-down deflections (quite unrelated to their static wheel alignment settings).

Upwards deflections are called jounce, and downwards deflections are called rebound. The suspension linkages determine the front and rear roll centers, which are two of the most important suspension design parameters.

Roll Centers

Roll centers assume their greatest importance in their relationship to the center of gravity. Since the centrifugal forces set up by driving the car around a curve act through the center of gravity, the car's cornering ability will be greater if it has a low center of gravity.

Just as the car turns, i.e., changes course, about its yaw axle, it rolls about its roll axis. The roll axis is the straight line between the front roll center and the rear roll center. Roll angles—that's the amount of lean or sway—are proportional to the vertical distance between the roll axis and the center of gravity.

The higher the center of gravity and the lower the roll axis, the great-

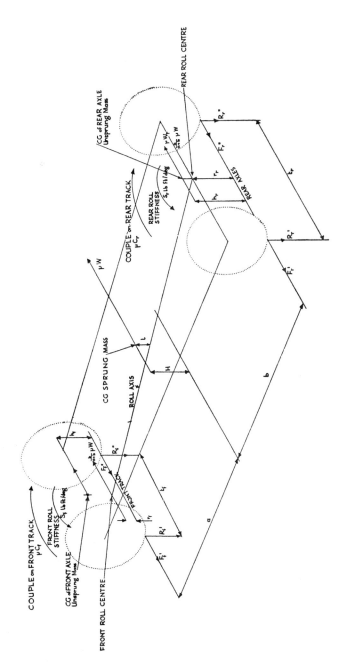

This diagram is used for calculating weight transfer.

33

er the roll angle under a given side force. Conversely, the higher the roll axis and the lower the center of gravity, the lesser the roll angle. All production cars roll in the direction of the side force, since the center of gravity is located above the roll axis.

The roll center is determined by the suspension design. Keep in mind that the front suspension system has no influence on the rear roll center, or vice versa. The only connection between the two is the roll axis, which, of course, is an abstraction.

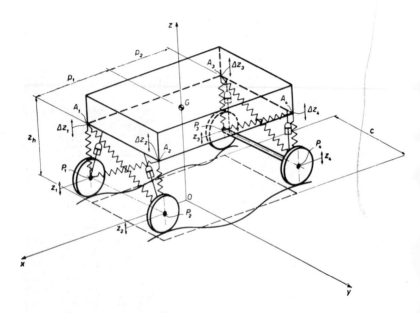

Vehicle dynamics model taking account of all known interacting design parameters can be mathematically "built" and tested on computers.

Let's start with the front suspension. Take the almost universal system, known in the industry as the SLA type: Short and Long Arm. The arms referred to are the control arms that guide the wheel. They are usually triangular, run crossways in the chassis and pivot up and down to allow the wheels to deflect.

To grasp the principle of SLA suspension, it is convenient to think of two triangles in two different horizontal planes, one above the other. In practice, the control arms are not parallel to each other, and neither one is horizontal in its static position. The inclination angles are carefully chosen to obtain the desired roll center height. The triangles pivot on their base lines, which are anchored on the front chassis cross member. Their tops are linked to ball joints on the front wheel spindle support arms, one upper and one lower.

Before the computer age, scale models were built and tested on special rigs, such as this Rover machine.

Before you can locate the roll center you've got to find the *instantaneous center*. That is the point of intersection between the continuations of the center lines (as seen from the front of the car) for both control arms of one wheel. Then you draw a dotted line from the instantaneous center to the center of the tire footprint. The roll center is located where this dotted line crosses the car's vertical center line.

Lengthening the upper or lower control arms has no effect on roll center height. It is only the pivot point location and the relative angles of the control arms that dictates roll center height. Lowering the lower control arm pivot shaft will lower the roll center. Lowering the upper control arm pivot shaft will raise the roll center.

To obtain a roll center location ground level, the pivot points must be closer together than the ball joints. If the vertical distance between the ball joints is greater than the vertical spacing between the control arm pivot shafts, the roll center will be placed below ground level.

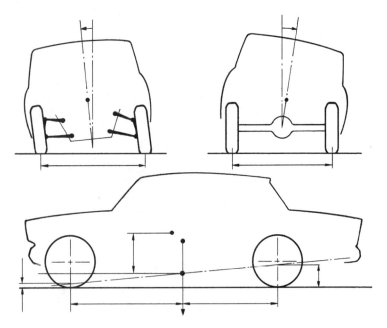

Center of gravity is displaced due to roll. Amount of roll depends on gravity center's height above roll axis.

Wheel deflections will inevitably result in camber changes on SLA systems. Most SLA control arms are so designed that the wheels maintain negative camber in all jounce positions and into the rebound area. Positive camber is usually detrimental to handling precision and is therefore avoided. Pronounced *negative camber* towards the end of the jounce travel is considered an advantage, as it tends to improve the cornering force of the tire in such situations. For instance, when taking a left curve at high speed, there is considerable weight transfer from the left to the right front wheel due to centrifugal force, plus some from each of the rear wheels due to the loss of speed during the maneuver. The added load compresses the right front spring, and the right front wheel, single-handedly keeping the car on its path, assumes a certain negative camber, bracing itself against the road surface.

Negative camber is of utmost importance when the wheel carries a high portion of the vehicle weight. A wheel that gets beyond a certain point on its rebound travel will logically be carrying very little load. It is there fore considered permissible for the front wheels to assume some *posit: ie camber* towards full rebound.

Camber changes are governed by lower control arm length, upper control arm length, and distance between the ball joints. Lengthening the upper control arm will reduce camber changes on deflection.

But not all independent front suspension systems are of the SLA type. There is another type that is quite popular (especially in Europe). It's the MacPherson system.

The MacPherson system is actually an SLA suspension *without an*

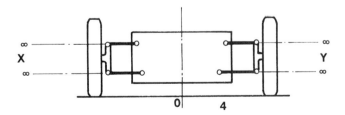

With SLA front suspension and parallel control arms, roll center is at ground level.

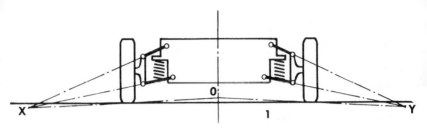

Higher tilt on upper control arm raises roll center above ground level.

upper control arm. Instead, it has a tall spring leg, standing on the lower (and only) control arm, and located on top in a spring tower aburment that forms part of the fender well or inner body structure. This leg works as an excellent locating member for the wheel and effectively replaces the upper control arm.

In the MacPherson front suspension system, the spindle support arm has no upper ball joint. Instead, its upper end forms a socket for the spring leg. The spring leg axis nearly coincides with the steering axis. The instantaneous center is determined by the continuation of the lower control arm center line and a line extending from the top of the spring strut at right angles to the spring strut axis. The instantaneous center is located where these lines intersect. The roll center is located where the line between the instantaneous center and the tire footprint center crosses the car's vertical center line.

Detail design changes can be made in the MacPherson suspension system to place the roll center at almost any height. Raising the control arm pivot axis will raise the roll center; lowering it will lower the roll center. Tilting the spring legs farther from vertical will raise the roll center; placing it closer to an upright position will lower the roll center.

And now, we'll look at the rear end. There are three principal types of rear suspension systems to consider:
1. Hotchkiss drive (rear axle with semi-elliptic leaf springs).
2. Axle suspension systems with positive link control.
3. Independent rear suspension.

There are two important advantages about axle suspensions: low manufacturing cost and totally predictable behavior. In addition American roads are being improved all the time, and the need for independent rear suspension (which offers highly improved road-holding) is gradually diminishing in the U.S.

One basic disadvantage of the beam axle is that, when one wheel rises over a bump or drops down into a hole, one end of the axle moves up or down and the camber angle of the wheel changes. Furthermore, because the two wheels are tied together by the axle beam, the other wheel is also affected. Its camber angle also changes.

On cars with Hotchkiss drive, the springs take on the axle locating duties as well as the normal springing and load-carrying functions. They take the driving thrust and whatever braking loads the rear wheels produce. Normally the springs are slung tightly under the axle housing and attached via U-bolts on both sides, as far apart as possible. The closer the leaf springs are to the wheels, the more stability you get.

The springs give the axle the freedon it needs to move up and down;

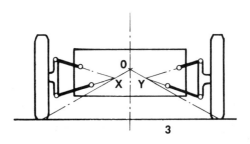

Opposite tilt on upper and lower control arms as shown can raise roll center to same height as center of gravity, thereby eliminating roll.

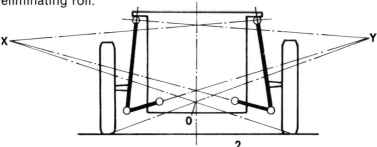

Roll center height in McPherson suspension is dictated by inward tilt of spring legs.

one wheel up and the other down, or both up and down together. They permit some fore-and-aft motion in the axle—which causes a rear wheel steering tendency when one wheel is twisted forward and the other backward. The leaf springs cannot positively prevent sideways movement in the axle under a side force, and they do not eliminate axle rotation around the drive shaft axis.

Axle-and-leaf spring suspension is still quite common. The shortcomings of the springs when used as control arms are not obvious in low-powered cars. In high-powered cars, the springs are stiffened to give adequate results, or they are supplemented by traction bars. There are two kinds of torque reaction in the axle. The axle housing tends to revolve in the opposite direction of the ring gear's rotation. It also tends to swing around in the opposite direction of the pinion's rotation. The first kind of torque reaction causes a lift in the pinion shaft on acceleration and bends the spring into an S-shape. This is called *spring windup,* and usually affects the left spring more than the right. Un-even spring windup twists the axle in the chassis and causes rear wheel steering.

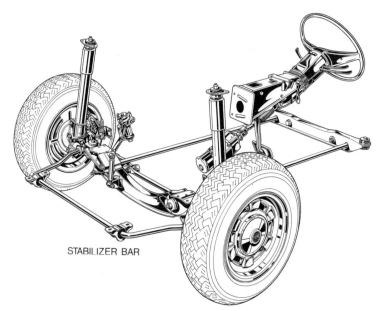

STABILIZER BAR

Stabilizer bar ends are attached to lower control arms, while center of bar is anchored to the frame.

The other kind of torque reaction tends to lift the right wheel on acceleration while pressing the left one harder to the road surface. This causes *axle tramp* (a periodic jumping up and down of the right wheel—even on a smooth surface) and leads to loss of traction. That means wheelspin. To regain traction, the driver has to back off on the accelerator. The left wheel has extra traction until the right wheel starts to spin, and this is what makes the left spring more susceptible to windup than the right one. Windup ends when wheel-spin sets in.

Some cars with leaf-spring axle suspension use a *track bar* to control sideways movement of the axle. The track bar is linked to the axle at its right-hand end and connected to the body structure at its left-hand end. This track bar will resist sideways movement of the axle relative to the body in directing tension or compression. With Hotchkiss drive, the roll center is located at spring anchorage height.

The same forces are at work in a rear axle located by a positive link system (with coil springs). However, this axle has all the up-and-

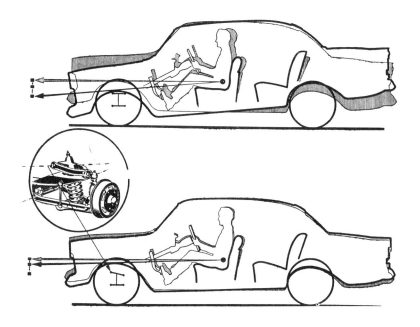

Anti-dive effect is produced by tilting the upper control arm in an SLA suspension system.

down freedom it needs but no freedom to turn, twist or move sideways. As a rule, there are two lower control arms, long and running forward from the axle in the fore-and-aft plane, plus two upper control arms, shorter and splayed at a fairly wide angle.

With this type of rear axle suspension, the roll center is located at linkage anchorage height. Roll stiffness is usually quite similar to that obtained with leaf-spring axle suspensions. Lateral axle location is assured by a track rod which runs across the chassis. One end of the track rod is attached to a bracket on the right side of the frame or body structure. If the axle tries to move right, it tends to stretch the track rod.

If the axle tries to move left, it tends to compress the track rod. The rod, made of solid steel, does not stretch or compress. As the axle moves up and down, the rod forces it to change position sideways by pulling it to the left towards full jounce or rebound. However, this is a precisely controlled sideways movement and therefore not detrimental to handling characteristics.

Independent rear suspension offers six principal advantages: Lower unsprung weight, absence of torque effect in the propeller shaft, elimination of torque reactions in the rear suspension, reduced sideways push during single-wheel deflection, space saving in the trunk area, and freedom to lower the roll center.

Since the axle housing is eliminated, unsprung weight is considerably reduced. This means an improved ride and promises improved handling precision.

Since the final drive unit is bolted to the frame, there can be no torque effect in the propeller shaft. This means improved traction in extreme conditions. Since there is no axle and the wheel hubs are positively located by control arms, there is no torque reaction in the rear suspension.

This means that axle tramp and loss of traction are eliminated. The complete elimination of wheel hop and shake in driving wheels depends on design detail, such as the control arm angles and anchorage points, maximum wheel travel, and spring rates. Since the rear wheels are not connected to each other, one wheel cannot push the other sideways when it hits a bump. This limits rear wheel steering effects.

Roll center height in independent rear suspension systems varies as greatly as in front suspensions, because the variables are just as many. There are only three modern "families" of independent rear suspension: SLA with the drive shaft working as upper control arms; SLA with splined drive shafts; and semi-trailing lower control arm with spring legs. The first and seconds types are adaptations of the SLA front suspension to the rear wheels and resemble modern front-drive suspension systems. The third type is an adaptation to the rear wheels of the MacPherson system (often referred to as a Chapman strut, since the Lotus designer, Colin Chapman, was first to use it). As with MacPherson suspension, roll center height depends on the tilt of the struts.

The De Dion axle is not a form of independent rear suspension but a costly and sophisticated type of driving wheel suspension. The final drive housing is bolted to the frame, and the drive shafts have both inner and outer universal joints. Sounds like independent rear suspension?

ROAD FORCES IN THE FRONT SUSPENSION

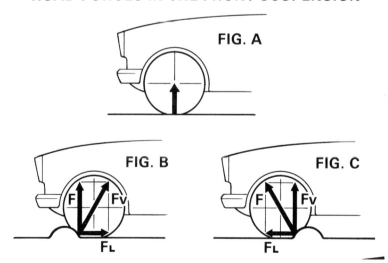

Normal road load is vertical (Fig. A). When car moves forward, bumps introduce a horizontal component (Fig. B) which changes direction when the car is driven in reverse (Fig. C).

No, because the hub carriers of each rear wheel are connected by a strong tube that keeps the wheels at permanent zero camber (unless set with slight negative camber), and maintains constant track. The tube is called a De Dion axle because it originated on De Dion Bouton cars about 1896. Its center usually carries a short locating stud that runs in a vertical groove on the back of the final drive housing. This locates the wheels laterally in relation to the chassis.

Fore-and-aft location of the wheels varies between the various cars that use De Dion axles. Some have parallel control arms, just like some rear axle suspension systems. Others have a Watt linkage. It is called that because James Watt invented it and used it for a mechanical link system in connection with steam engines.

The Watt linkage consists of a vertical link pivoted in its center, with a forward control arm attached to its lower end and a rearward control arm attached to its upper end. When the pivot point moves up, the link is no longer vertical, as the upper end is pulled backwards and the lower end is pulled forwards. Both ends move in opposite directions by equal amounts, but—and this is the key to its use in suspension systems—the pivot point describes a strictly vertical motion. Watt linkages are also used on some cars to control sideways axle movement (replacing the simple track rod location system).

The roll center of a De Dion suspension system depends on the height of the lateral location point. If the De Dion tube runs at hub level, the roll center will tend to be about hub level. With a lower De Dion tube, the roll center can be lowered. The De Dion axle has none of the drawbacks of the common rear axle but it enjoys the same advantages (low camber changes, high roll center and restricted weight transfer).

THE SPRINGS
Theory of Springing
The springs play an important part in handling, but their major duties lie in the area of ride. The springs have an effect on roll stiffness, as we have seen, and they also influence the ratio of sprung to unsprung weight (since part of each spring is deflected with the road wheel).

Springing action should be as soft as possible for the best ride comfort. Road shocks should be "swallowed" and not transmitted to the vehicle. Springing action should also be progressive, taking a bump in the roadway softly at first and then gradually hardening towards the end of the deflection. Springing action should assure evenness of ride regardless of vehicle load, which is an almost impossible goal if the car has conventional metallic springs.

Any impact on a road wheel attached to an automobile will be transmitted to the spring, from the spring to the frame, and eventually the impact forces will be distributed throughout the entire structure. The reaction to impact depends mainly upon spring properties. Modern cars use low-rate springs which deflect considerably under a given load in order to provide a high level of ride comfort.

Ride is mainly a matter of carrying the vertical loads in the car and insulating the occupants from dynamic forces originated by the road surface. Ride comfort is largely governed by vehicle balance, static deflections and frequencies. Spring rates are developed to produce a well-balanced or flat ride, free of pitch and within a reasonable frequency range. The springs carry the static load and absorb road shocks.

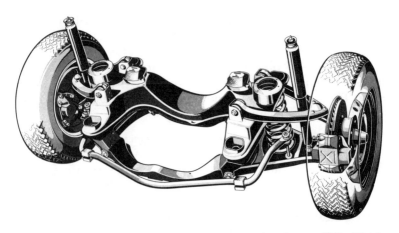

SLA front suspension used on Mercedes-benz 350 SL has springs mounted on lower control arm.

SLA front suspension used on the Fiat 125 carried springs on top of the upper control arm.

The stiffness or softness of springs is usually expressed in pounds per inch (lb/in) at the wheel (pounds of load against inches of wheel travel). This is called the wheel rate. This rate denotes the forces necessary to provoke a one-inch upward deflection of the wheel—which is not the same as a one-inch compression of the spring. The wheel rate takes the suspension linkage into account, and reflects a truer picture of spring action.

The suspension travel is the total vertical wheel movement allowed by the springs, suspension linkage and body. A large amount of travel allows big bumps and dips to be traversed with soft springs. Limiting the travel means the suspension can be "bottomed" easily unless the wheel rates are raised. As a general rule, the greater the sprung weight, the more vertical movement is needed. Wheel travel, however, is limited by fender shape, body design, and overall vehicle height.

If stiffly sprung sports cars usually handle well, this is due more to

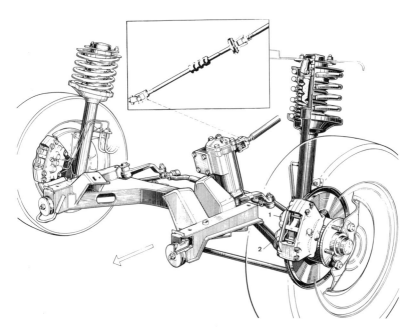

McPherson suspension system used on BMW Bavaria uses spring leg as both upper control arm and steering axis.

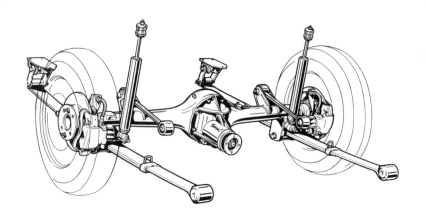

Axle suspension of Fiat 125 has traction bars in addition to leaf springs.

their high roll frequency, with resultant quick steering response and low roll amplitudes, than to superior design. But stiff springs reduce tire adhesion by resisting deflection and thus often cause the tires to lose contact with the road surface entirely. In consequence, reasonably low spring rates are a necessity for both handling characteristics and ride comfort. But wheel rates is not the only measure of spring action. There is another criterion, which is probably more basic, and that is suspension frequency.

Suspension frequency is the frequency at which the sprung mass will oscillate freely when deflected. Suspension frequencies range from zero to the limits of audible noise. It applies to all types of frames and bodies that low-frequency motions up to 10 cycles per second are ride motions. Between 10 and 30 cycles we have shake (beaming, torsional shake, and cross-shake). Low amplitude vibration sets in at 30 cycles, and above 150 cycles we have "periods" of vibration—the frequency is so high that no motion is felt but the vibration is audible.

Ride motions are controlled by the spring ride rates. Ride rates are chosen to give the vehicle occupants acceptable ride comfort, and represent a compromise between amplitude and frequency. Amplitude means travel (up and down movement of the wheel), and frequency means the time taken to complete one spring action cycle—from the start of deflection until the spring returns to normal.

It is a general truth (but not absolute) that the lower the frequency, the better the ride comfort. The problem is that low frequency involves low spring rates, which indicates a need for large amplitude. And large amplitudes are not always possible (due to space limitations, or limitations in the suspension geometry.)

Ride motion frequencies are usually measured in cycles per minute rather than cycles per second. Most American cars have ride frequencies between 60 and 100 cycles per minute. Some luxury cars have lower frequencies—down to 52 cycles per minute, which is about as low as you can reasonably go with metal springs. Many European cars—sports cars in particular—have ride frequencies up to 150-180 cycles per minute. Such high frequencies are acceptable only at very small amplitudes.

With non-metal springs ride frequencies can be reduced as low as 40 cycles per minute.

American Motors axle suspension has four-link control.

Shake is governed by three factors: the suspension, the engine, and the structure. In a full-size car their frequencies occur within a close cycle range—usually about 12 per second. And the engine mass can actually be used as an absorbing element to control shake.

For compact cars the natural frequencies are higher—18 to 20 cycles per second—and the engines are often too light to serve as shake absorbers. Vibrations caused by the engine and drive train can usually be isolated by careful attention to mountings (engine mounting roll axis must coincide with the torque axis of the engine), the cables and the linkages.

When discussing human discomfort, it becomes necessary to distinquish between cyclical oscillation and random shock. Random shock will produce no illness symptoms in the average passenger, but it is of course an unpleasant experience which suspension engineers strive to eliminate.

On the other hand, human beings are extremely sensitive to cyclical motions. Low-frequency oscillations such as ride motions of less

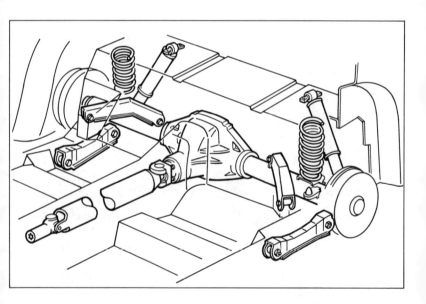

Chevrolet Vega axle suspension has four-link control with ultra-short arms widely spaced.

than two cycles per second sometimes cause travel sickness. Other ride motions usually cause nothing more severe than travel fatigue (by triggering involuntary use of muscles). Shake can also have tiring effects, but vibration is mainly to be considered as an annoyance (which causes different reactions in different people).

The human body can tolerate high-amplitude body displacements, especially when the displacements occur at low frequency. High-frequency vibrations can be tolerated as long as amplitude is low.

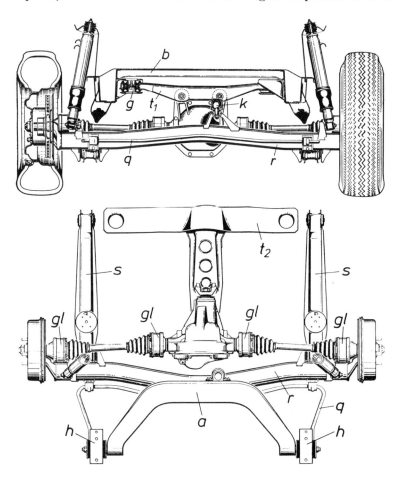

De Dion suspension as used on Opel Admiral is not fully independent and keeps wheels vertical at all times.

Ride comfort is mostly a matter of selecting the right combinations of wheel rates, frequency, and suspension travel.

Metal Springs

The basic type of metal spring is the leaf spring. Automotive leaf springs usually consist of several length of steel strip cut from the same roll, assembled by lamination and joined by a bolt through their geometrical center and clamped together. Only the main leaf has eyes for mounting pins or shackles. The extremities of the supporting leaves are usually square-cut.

One advantage of the leaf spring is that inter-leaf friction dampens its deflections, constituting a built-in shock absorber. Leaf springs continue to provide an inexpensive springing medium but they have fallen into disfavor on modern passenger cars mainly because of their shortcomings as locating members.

All metal springs utilize the elasticity of steel for their basic functions. While the leaf spring flexes under stress in direct tension, coil springs and torsion bars are stressed in shear. Coil springs and torsion bars have no inherent damping effect, but work better than leaf springs in absorbing minute road irregularities (since there is no initial friction to overcome), and also permit larger deflections.

As normally installed in an automobile, all springs have a constant rate of compressibility. But various degrees of variable rates (rising with increasing loads) have been used.

Non-Metal Springs

Three successful types of unconventional springing are used on European cars. All three provide automatic level control, and two of them require no additional shock absorbers. All three systems are applied to all four wheels. One system has simple air springs (Mercedes-Benz); the second system combines air and oil Citroen); and the third system combines rubber, water and alcohol (British Leyland—Hydrolastic).

All pneumatic springs work on the principle of the compressibility of gases. That provides flexibility. The function of an air cylinder is somewhat like a tire pump as used for bicycles, with the cylinder attached to the chassis frame and the piston rod attached to the control arm. The weight of the vehicle increases the initial pressure until the column of air will support its static weight. The piston stroke is long enough to permit further pressure during bump conditions and to tolerate pressure drops on rebound.

The air spring unit consists of a constant-volume air chamber with a flexible rubber diaphragm at the bottom. The diaphragm is connected to a piston attached to the lower control arm, and the air in the chamber is compressed on jounce deflections of the wheel.

The air-and-oil spring unit is a spherical container with a flexible rubber diaphragm that separates the gas element of the system from the oil-based element. The static weight of the car and the suspension movements are sustained by nitrogen gas under pressure in the cylinder on which the spherical container is mounted. The effective length of the suspension leg is dictated by the amount of oil in the cylinder. The oil volume also controls the height of the car above the ground and its automatic levelling. The oil works as a damper (shock absorber) on all suspension movements. The damping action is obtained by fitting a two-way restrictor valave between the cylinder and the spherical container. The lamination of the fluid reduces the flow rate, with the result that movements are continuous and progressive, and always proportional to the speed of fluid displacement.

The hydrolastic chamber is filled with a water-and-alcohol mixture. When the piston rod is driven upward by Jounce deflection of the wheel, the diaphragm flexes and displaces water through the damper restriction. As the volume of the cylinder is reduced by the motion

Independent rear suspension of Mercedes 350 SL has semi-trailing arms with moderate camber changes during deflection.

of the piston, the rubber is correspondingly deformed by the pressure of the liquid. The cylinder, diaphragm and rubber springs are so shaped that the volume of liquid displaced increases at a higher rate than the linear increase of piston stroke. As a result, the rubber spring offers a progressively increasing resistance to load. Water was chosen instead of an oil-based liquid because of the constant viscosity of water at all normal operating temperatures.

One of the problems with metal springs is that adding load uses up part of the spring travel. That means less than the normal amount of travel is available for taking bumps when the car is fully loaded (with its full complement of passengers and luggage).

Consequently, many car makers use variable-rate springs, which have a higher rate (stiffer action) the closer they get to full deflection. This has the effect of gradually restricting wheel travel and minimizing the risk of bottoming.

Non-metal spring systems have automatic levelling and are therefore unaffected by changes in load. They provide full wheel travel and constant ride rates and frequency regardless of how many occupants are in the car or much luggage is carried.

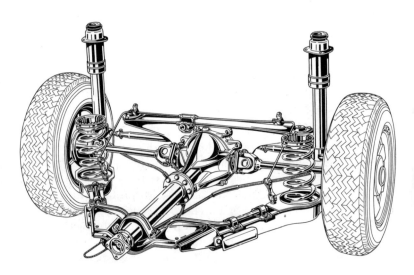

Independent rear suspension of Fiat 130 has semi-trailing arms and more ample camber changes during deflection.

Beefing up Your Springs

"Beefing up" your springs is one of the most basic areas of chassis tuning. Going to higher-rate (stiffer) springs will reduce suspension travel and raise the ride frequency. More important—and more advantageous—they will give increased roll stiffness. Any form of chassis tuning is intimately concerned with understeer and oversteer, and there are some general rules concerning changes in spring rates.

The front/rear balance is extremely important. Going to stiffer front springs will cause stronger understeer (all other things remaining equal). Installing softer front springs will cause less pronounced understeers. Softer rear springs will strengthen any understeering tendency.

Most auto makers offer heavy-duty springs, and a number of auto equipment stores and mail-order businesses have large stocks of beefed-up springs for most popular makes and models. For catalog and prices, write to:

J. C. Whitney & Co., 1917-19 Archer Avenue, Chicago, Ill. 60616
FAZA, 82 North Main Street, Brewster, N.Y. 10509
Jerrari Equipment, P.O. Box 283, Redondo Beach, Calif. 90277
Rich Motors, 1615 South Brand, Glendale, Calif. 91204
BRE/Interpart, 141 Oregon, El Segundo, Calif. 90245
Endurance Racing Enterprises, Box 266, Hermosa Beach, Calif. 90254

For cars with rear axles and semi-elliptic leaf springs, traction bars are recommended. They are simple control arms designed to aid the springs in their axle locating duties.

They run in the fore-and-aft plane between the axle housing and the nearest frame cross-member ahead of the axle. They maintain constant parallelity between the axle and the anchorage points and prevent rear wheel steering. They keep the axle from moving so as to cause spring windup, and they alleviate the lift problem in the right rear wheel. They have little or no effect on sideways movement of the axle. For cars not fitted with traction bars from the factory, they are available as an accessory and can easily be added. Traction bars have no effect on roll stiffness, rides rates or suspension travel.

For cars that roll excessively, stabilizer bars can provide the answer. Almost all production cars have a front stabilizer bar, and a few have a rear stabilizer bar as well. If roll stiffness is inadequate, the usual remedy is to fit a stronger (heavier) front stabilizer bar and install a rear stabilizer. Again, the front/rear roll stiffness relationship must be kept in mind, for that is what controls weight transfer.

As a general rule, a heavier front stabilizer bar will give stronger understeer. A stabilizer bar added to the rear suspension on a car which does not have one as standard will reduce the understeering tendency. A heavier rear stabilizer bar (on a car that has one as standard) will lessen the understeer.

Traction bars and stabilizer bars for all popular makes and models are available from the same organizations that offer beefed-up springs.

SHOCK ABSORBERS
Theory of Damping

All metallic springs require the help of a shock absorber to control spring action. Just what does the shock absorber do? It's easier to explain what it doesn't do. It does not absorb shocks, for one thing. The spring is the element that cushions the shock. The shock absorber is just a brake on the spring to keep it from continuing its spring action. As the engineers would say it: the shock absorber dampens the resonance bands of wheel jounce and rebound to bring an end to the oscillation.

The shock absorbers should really be renamed spring dampers. Without shock absorbers, a spring supporting a given load, when triggered by a deflection caused by outside impact, will bounce at a natural frequency, much in the manner of a trampoline. Shock absorbers speed up the recovery of the static position of the spring. Without shock absorbers, there would consequently be a great risk of vibration in the wheels themselves, not caused by rotational imbalance, but by deflections, manifesting itself as a fast vertical oscillation of the individual wheels which could upset the steering geometry and the entire balance of the car.

In a typical shock absorber, the compression resistance is considerably lower than the rebound resistance. That's because the shock absorber is not intended to fight the bumps, but to limit other spring movements to a minimum.

How much resistance is wanted in the shock absorber depends on the car. First, its weight—sprung and unsprung. Then, the suspen-

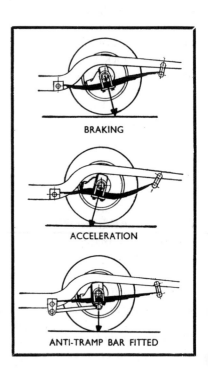

BRACKING

ACCELERATION

ANTI-TRAMP BAR FITTED

Traction bars restrict spring windup and axle tramp.

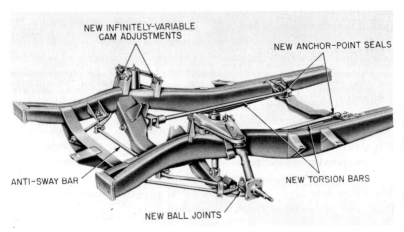

NEW INFINITELY-VARIABLE CAM ADJUSTMENTS

NEW ANCHOR-POINT SEALS

ANTI-SWAY BAR

NEW TORSION BARS

NEW BALL JOINTS

Torsion bars are just coil springs straightened out. In this Chrysler suspension, they are twisted by the lower control arm pivot axis.

sion linkage. If the suspension is so designed that shock absorber travel is less than wheel travel for a given bump, the shock absorber must be correspondingly beefed up. The relationship between wheel travel and shock absorber movement is called link ratio, and the required resistance in the shock absorber rises as the square of the link ratio. A car with a 1.8 : 1 link ratio needs damping characteristics with 36 percent higher strength than a car of similar weight with a 1.2 : 1 link ratio.

The car owner usually has no means to alter the link ratio. But in his chassis tuning efforts, he may undertake a number of modifications that changes the car's damping requirements. If you install stronger springs (higher spring rates) it's increasingly important to get a shock absorber with higher rebound resistance. Stiffer springs tend to return the wheel to the road harder and faster, but this is not desirable, as it tends to set up a reaction that can give rise to a second bump motion well after the bump has been passed. If you keep the standard springs but fit bigger wheels and tires, you are adding to the unsprung weight, and will require more jounce resistance.

Shock Absorber Construction

The shock absorber is a telescopic unit partially filled with hydraulic fluid. It is mounted concentrically with the coil spring on many cars. On other cars it is mounted separately. The shock absorber consists of two concentric tubes, a piston and rod, and valves for controlling hydraulic resistance. The inner tube is a pressure tube. It works as a cylinder in which the piston operates. The upper end is sealed by a piston rod seal. The lower end is closed by the compression valve assembly. Resistance to fluid motion inside the shock absorber imposes a restriction on its compression or extension and gives the required dampening effect on the spring action.

It is also called "foot valve" since it is located at the base of the unit, or "bump valve" since this is where jounce movements (bumps) are resisted. The inner tube is completely filled with fluid at all times. The outer tube works as a reservoir. It provides space for reserve fluid and for overflow from the pressure tube.

Rebound forces are resisted by the piston, through the action of its relief valve and by-pass valve. The piston rod (and the outer tube) which form the upper end of the shock absorber, are attached to the vehicle—frame or unit body. The pressure tube, i.e. the lower end, is attached to the suspension linkage.

The main design parameter for shock absorbers is size (as defined by piston diameter). Shock absorbers that are great for a light car will be intolerably adequate on a heavy car. No matter how the insides of the shock absorbers are designed and calibrated, there's no substitute for size.

Shock Absorber Action
As the wheel moves up and down, the spring is compressed or elongated. Simultaneously the shock absorber is telescoped or extended. The action of the shock absorber forces the fluid to move two ways:
1. between the pressure tube and the reservoir tube, and
2. between the upper and lower sides of the piston.

There are only two movements in the shock absorber—compression (bump) and extension (rebound). To keep each condition separate in your mind, we'll deal separately with shock absorber action in each case.

Bump (Jounce) Action
Compression of the shock absorber drives the piston down. This raises hydraulic pressure in the lower end of the inner tube. Fluid

British Leyland's Hydrolastic suspension is used on the Austin Maxi.

escapes along two different paths: (A) through the compression valve to the reservoir, and (B) through the relief valve in the piston to the top end of the pressure tube.

The task of the relief valve is to equalize pressure on both sides of the piston. Fluid flow through the relief valve is controlled by the number of orifices in the valve and their diameter. The compression valve offers little resistance on flow to the reservoir.

Rebound Action
When spring action returns the wheel to the ground, the shock absorber is extended. This raises the pressure in the upper end of the pressure tube, and lowers the pressure at the bottom end. Now, the relief valve is closed, and remains closed. It's a one-way passage for upward flow only. Instead, downward flow is directed through the bypass valve, which has quite different construction.

The bypass valve itself is a ring with a rill (a circular groove) screwed into the piston. The valve is spring-loaded against its base. Rill size controls low-velocity flow resistance (large rill = more fluid flow = less dampening).

The flow path is through the piston rod, via one large radial orifice at the top, and a circular arrangement of rod holes inside the piston which in turn connects with the pressure side of the bypass valve.

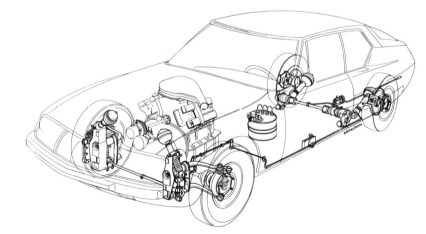

Oleo-pneumatic suspension on Citroen SM is controlled by a central hydraulic system.

The size of the rod holes controls high-velocity flow resistance.

During this process, the compression valve at the lower end acts as a suction valve, and admits fluid from the reservoir to enter the pressure tube.

Adjustable Shock Absorbers

Most shock absorbers have no adjustment possibilities. They either have the proper characteristics for the car, or they don't. If you are tuning your chassis, going to adjustable shock absorbers is one of the first steps you should take. They enable you to change the rebound resistance. Racing-type shock absorbers also have jounce adjustment, but for road use, rebound adjustment is generally all that's needed. Adjustable shock absorbers also enable you to maintain the original damping characteristics throughout their life.

Standard shock absorbers must be junked when worn. Adjustable shock absorbers can wear out, too, but wear is concentrated in one place: where the piston rubs against the tube. This gives rise to leakage, and in a standard shock absorber, there's nothing to be done about it short of replacing the whole unit. Adjustable shock absorbers can be tightened up to compensate for this leakage.

The adjuster is mounted at the lower end of the piston, mounted on a screw threaded into the bottom end of the piston rod. Turning the adjuster clockwise drives the screw deeper into the rod, which blocks off one of the rod holes feeding the bypass valve. Continued turning will block off more rod holes, which adds rebound resistance.

Koni shock absorbers, which are the best known of all adjustable units, have several types with external adjustment. Adjustment is performed at the top, with a small wrench or an Allen key. For Koni literature and prices, write to Kensington Products, 150 Green Street, Hackensack, New Jersey 07601.

Load Levelers

A load leveler is a shock absorber surrounded by a coil spring. The unit is installed as a regular shock absorber in special applications where higher spring rates are desired. Naturally, the load leveler also adds to roll stiffness. It can be an enormous help for cars with low ride rates and excessive suspension amplitudes. It can also detract from the proper and necessary spring deflections on some cars, and must therefore be installed with a good deal of discrimination.

The existence of the auxiliary coil spring reduces the demand for bump resistance in the shock absorber, but adds to the need for rebound damping. Many shock absorber manufacturers now offer load levelers:

Koni (Kensington Products, 150 Green Street, Hackensack, N.J. 07601).

Motorcraft (formerly Autolite—available from Ford and Lincoln-Mercury dealers)

Monroe (Monroe Auto Equipment Company, Monroe, Michigan 48161).

Hydro-Pneumatic Shock Absorbers

On a growing number of cars, the rear shock absorbers are combined with air springs to assure *automatic level control.* Such shock absorbers are normal telescopic units with a pliable nylon reinforced neoprene boot acting as an air chamber. The unit will extend when

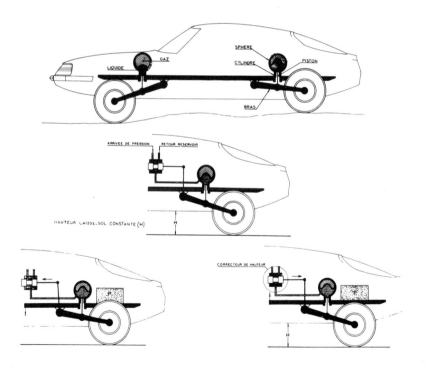

The SM suspension provides automatic level control.

inflated and deflation will make it retract. The two shock absorbers are interconnected via a flexible air line that equalizes pressure in the two air chambers. An eight to 15 psi air pressure is maintained in the air chambers at all times in order to minimize boot friction.

This is accomplished by a check valve in the exhaust fitting on the control valve. The system is so designed that in the event of air pressure loss, shock absorber function and the action of the conventional rear springs will continue without being impaired.

The system consists of an air compressor, a reservoir tank, pressure regulator assembly, height control valve, link, special shock absorbers and flexible air lines. The compressor is a two-stage, vacuum actuated type, requiring no lubrication. Vacuum supply is taken from the engine carburetor base. The compressor's first stage draws air at atmospheric pressure through a one-way check valve. The second stage feeds high-pressure air to the reservoir tank.

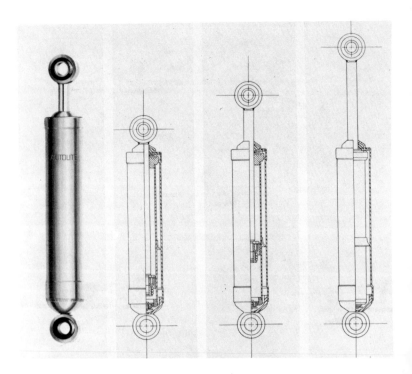

Standard shock absorber with 1-inch piston diameter.

On the first stage compression stroke, the intake valve is closed, and the check valve in the second stage end of the piston is opened. This allows air from the first stage cylinder to flow out through the hollow piston into the second stage cylinder for high pressure compression. The second stage compression stroke closes the check valve in the piston and opens the check valve in the end of the second stage housing.

Intake and compression strokes are controlled by a sliding distributor valve. The valve is actuated through an arm that is tripped by the piston as it nears the end of each stroke. Each time the arm actuates the distributor valve, a different set of holes are covered in the first stage housing. The distributor valve controls the flow of intake manifold vacuum and air under atmospheric pressure—alternately on opposite sides of the compressor diaphragm.

As the compressor runs, the reservoir air pressure gradually builds

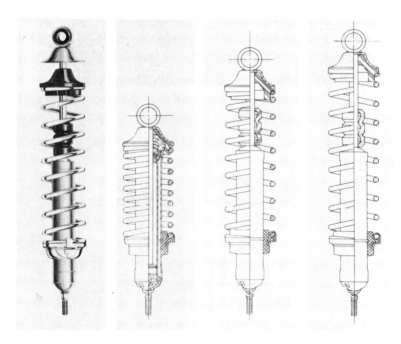

Shock absorber with overload springs is intended for rear wheel installation.

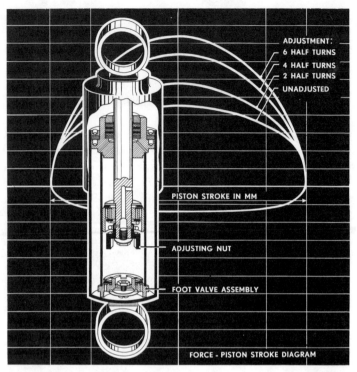

ADJUSTMENT:
6 HALF TURNS
4 HALF TURNS
2 HALF TURNS
UNADJUSTED

PISTON STROKE IN MM

ADJUSTING NUT

FOOT VALVE ASSEMBLY

FORCE - PISTON STROKE DIAGRAM

Koni adjustable shock absorber has four different settings for rebound resistance.

De Carbon pressurized shock absorber has a gas chamber at the lower end of the unit.

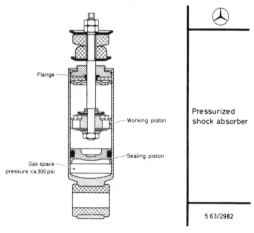

Flange

Working piston

Sealing piston

Gas space
pressure ca 300 psi

Pressurized
shock absorber

5 63/2982

Delco Superlift shock absorbers provide automatic level control.

up. This gives rise to a back pressure on the second stage piston until it equals the push or pressure against the diaphragm. At this point, the system is in a balanced condition and the unit stops operating. When action in the system reduces reservoir pressure, the compressor resumes its function and refills the reservoir. Pressure balance will depend on the prevailing manifold vacuum and atmospheric pressure. Both are affected by altitude (above sea level). The pressure regulator valve is preset and limits the reservoir outlet pressure to avoid damage to the height control valve and shock absorbers.

The height control valve is mounted on the frame. It senses rear car height through a link attached to the right rear upper control arm. When load is added, the overtravel level is forced up. This brings an internal lever to open the intake valve. When this valve is open, high pressure air is admitted to the shock absorber air chambers. As the car is raised, the intake valve shuts. When load is removed, the overtravel lever is forced down, causing the internal arm to open the exhaust valve. When the car is lowered to level position, the exhaust valve shuts. To prevent air transfer under normal road movements, a four to 15 seconds delay mechanism is built into the height control valve. The overtravel lever, which pivots around the control valve shaft, rides off the flat side of the control shaft and does not have time to react to the high-frequency changes of ride motions.

STEERING
Theory of Steering

We have seen in earlier chapters that all four wheels play a part in steering the car, but that is not what we are talking about when we are discussing the steering system. The steering system has one purpose and one purpose only: control of the front wheels. That sounds simple enough. But there are some bothersome facts, as you will see. For instance, the front wheels are mounted on opposite sides of the car. That means that they do not travel the same distance when going around a curve. They do not follow the same arc, and they must be steered at different angles (just as the rear wheels have a differential to enable them to be driven around turns at different speeds).

The inside front wheel takes a sharper turn than the outside front wheel, and the steering system must be designed to give it a higher steering angle than the outside wheel, in proportion to the severity of the turn. How this is accomplished will be explained a little later. First we have to look at the basics of front wheel alignment, which is an essential part of all steering duties.

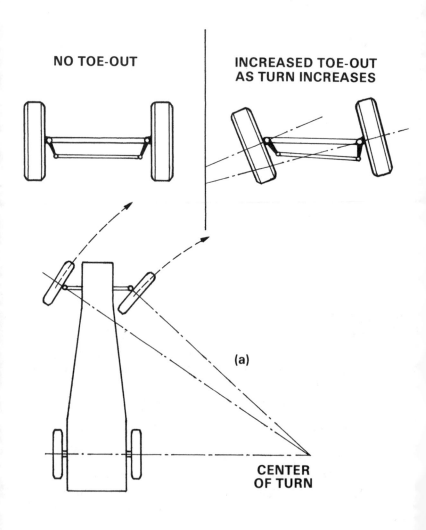

NO TOE-OUT

**INCREASED TOE-OUT
AS TURN INCREASES**

(a)

**CENTER
OF TURN**

Non-parallel steering arms provide increased toe-out with in-creased steering angles giving a common turn center for all wheels.

Static Wheel Alignment

The main purpose of wheel alignment is to make the wheels roll without scuffing, dragging or slipping under all road operating conditions. This gives greater safety in driving, easier steering, longer tire wear and less strain on the parts that make up the front end of the automobile. Static wheel alignment is dictated by five simple angles. They are toe-in, camber, caster, steering axis inclination, and turning radius.

These angles are designed into the car by the manufacturer for the purpose of assuring proper distribution of weight on the moving parts and to facilitate the steering functions. The front wheels are not set parallel to each other. They do not stand straight up and they do not point straight ahead. There are good reasons for this. The front wheels tend to *toe-out* at speed. A small toe-in angle is necessary to counteract this. Wheels that toe-out would be aimed to the sides—the left wheel to the left and the right wheel to the right. Toe-in is the opposite. Wheels that toe-in would collide if they were allowed to go where they are aimed.

Why is toe-in necessary? When the car starts rolling forward, rolling resistance and wind resistance try to push the wheels back, i.e., to the rear of the car. The suspension system holds one side of the wheel and keeps it from going backwards.

But it cannot keep it perfectly aligned. Wear in the suspension and steering parts created many sources of minute play. They combine into giving the wheel some form of freedom to toe-out at speed.

The purpose of toe-in is simply to compensate for tolerances in the steering linkage. Naturally, toe-in is a cause of tread wear. Its tire wear appears as a feather-edged scuff across the face of both tires. However, it has been found that excessive toe-in will result in wear appearing on the outside of the right front tire only. Conversely, excessive toe-out will result in wear appearing on the inside of the left front tire only.

Toe-in with the vehicle in a stationary position is measured in inches. When measured with the wheel in motion on a scuff gauge, it is measured in feet of side slip per mile.

Toe-in angles vary with wheel deflections (due to changes in front suspension geometry) and suspension engineers try to minimize these toe-in changes, since excessive toe-out leads to loss of steering precision and wandering at high speeds. Naturally, toe-in changes also take place in roll (because the outside front spring is compressed and the inside front spring is stretched). Toe-in changes in roll are also kept to a minimum.

Toe-in is the last of the alignment angles to be set in any wheel alignment operation. It is adjusted by turning the tie rod adjusting sleeves until the measurements taken at the front of the wheels comply to the car manufacturer's specifications.

In theory, the front wheels should be parallel and vertical when the car is loaded and in motion. To obtain this, they are given a static setting with a small positive *camber angle*. Camber is the tilt of a wheel from its vertical position when viewed from the front. Camber will change under weight (passengers and load) to varying degrees

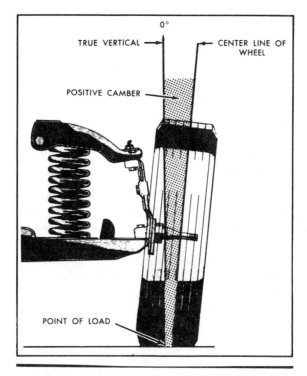

Camber angle is lateral tilt of wheel.

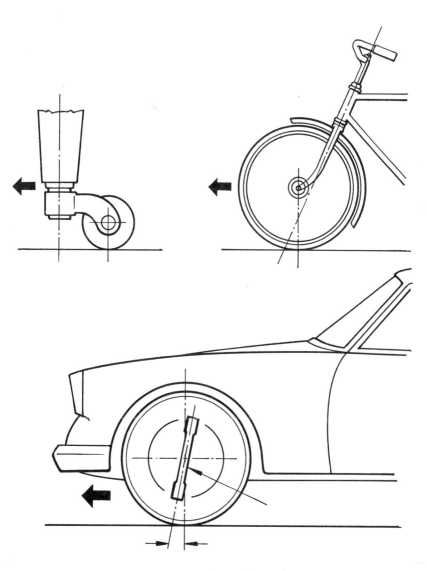

Caster angle is backward tilt of steering axis.

because of front suspension geometry. With SLA suspension, the top of the wheel is allowed to move in and out on deflections, while bottom remains in place.

Camber is measured in degrees and is the amount the center line of the wheel is tilted from true vertical. Outward tilt of the wheel at the top from true vertical is positive camber. Inward tilt of the wheel at the top from true vertical is negative camber. A slight positive camber setting is usually recommended to compensate for toe-in. Many sports cars have negative camber settings, since negative front wheel camber tends to reduce understeer. Adding more positive front wheel camber will strengthen the understeer.

Correct positive camber places the point of load inside the tire footprint, distributes the load on the wheel bearings, reduces tire scrub and eases the steering. No steering effort is necessary to keep the car going straight. The front wheels are given a certain amount of directional stability by a backwards tilt of the spindle support arm. This tilt angle is called *caster angle*. It can also be described as the angle between the spindle support arm ball joints and the vertical line through the wheel hub, viewed from the side. The caster angle is positive if the steering knuckle is tilted backwards at the top. Caster angle is negative if it is tilted forward at the top. Positive caster increases directional stability. Too much positive caster will make the wheels hard to turn. Correct positive caster tends to keep the wheels pointed straight ahead and helps straighten them after a turn.

Why is this? You can readily see that when the caster angle is zero (or vertical), there is no force, as a result of the caster angle, that tends to turn the wheels in either direction. However, if the caster angle is changed from zero to positive caster, forces are set up between the road surface and the tires that tend to bring the front wheels back to the straight-ahead position. As the caster angle is increased in the positive direction more effort will be required to steer the car away from a true course and hold it there. The tendency of the car to straighten out more rapidly when leaving a turn for the straight away is also increased by increasing positive caster.

Too high a positive camber angle is undesirable for a number of reasons, the most common of which are:

1. Excessive effort required to turn corners.
2. Indirect cause of low-speed shimmy.
3. Indirect cause of road shock.
4. Indirect cause of high-speed wander.

In recent years, many large American cars have been built with negative caster. That involves a loss of directional stability, which is more than made up for by the weight distribution in the cars, in combination with their pattern of camber changes in roll and high steering axis inclination. Why is negative center desirable? It offers lighter steering effort, improves parking ease, and minimizes road shock. Caster angles have no effect on understeer/oversteer. Caster angles remain constant during wheel deflection, regardless of suspension geometry.

Steering axis inclination is the inward tilt of the spindle support arm at the top. The steering axis is the line between the two ball joints. It is not vertical—it leans in at the top. At ground level, the steering axis hits the tire footprint off center.

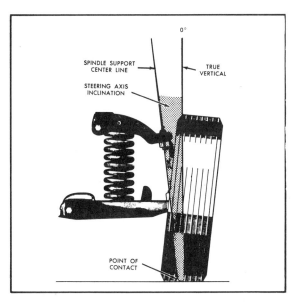

Steering axis inclination in inward tilt of steering axis. Point of contact shows scrub radius.

Steering axis inclination used to be called "king pin inclination" but king pins have been replaced by ball joints (one upper and one lower) that locate the spindle support arm.

The purposes of steering axis inclination are:
1. To reduce the need for excessive camber.
2. To distribute the weight of the vehicle on the spindle more nearly over the road contact of the tire.
3. To provide a pivot point on the tire on which the wheel will turn to provide easy steering.
4. To work with caster to aid steering stability.

Steering axis inclination is a directional control angle measured in degrees and is the amount the spindle support center line is tilted from true vertical. This angle is non-adjustable.

The front-wheel spindle is at its highest point when the car is traveling straight ahead. When turned, the spindle moves downward as a result of steering axis inclination. As the wheel and tire cannot be lowered, this has the effect of raising the front of the car. This occurs simultaneously on both sides. When the steering wheel is released the weight of the car will help the wheels resume a straight-ahead position. Steering axis inclination also controls the scrub radius of the front tires.

Scrub radius is the distance, at ground level, between the steering axis and the center of the tire footprint. Correct scrub radius combines directional stability with ease of turning at low speed, reduces tire scrub, and eliminates the need for a high camber angle.

Too long a scrub radius means hard steering. Too short a scrub radius means wandering and weaving. If the scrub radius is not identical on both front wheels, the car tends to pull to the side of the longest scrub radius. Scrub radius is positive if the steering axis hits the tire footprint inside of the center; negative if it hits outside of center. Most cars have positive scrub radius, but heavy front-drive cars have negative scrub radius.

Turning radius is the amount one front wheel turns sharper than the other on a turn. The inside front wheel turns shorter than the outside front wheel, creating a toe-out condition when the vehicle is turned either to the right or left. Correct turning radius allows the front tires to roll free on the turns. Consequently, turning radius will be correct when all other alignment angles are correct. The geometry that provides the correct turning radius involves the entire chassis.

When a car makes a turn, there is a point on the ground on the inside of the turn that becomes the turn center. Each wheel has its own turn radius. The turn radius can be defined as the distance between the turn center and the tire footprint center for each wheel. The inside front wheel has a shorter turn radius than the outside wheel. To run smoothly, the wheels must be at right angles to their turn radius.

The inside wheel is therefore turned at a higher steering angle. This is accomplished by proper design of the steering arms. Both steering arms have the same length and are placed at the same angle relative to the centerline of the car. They are angled so that they point towards an instantaneous center somewhere in back of the front seat and in front of the rear axle. Each front wheel must turn to the point where its axis simultaneously intersects the extended rear wheel axis and the other front wheel's axis.

When the tie rods move the steering arms, each steering arm describes an arc. But they do not describe the same arc, because their starting points were different. The right steering arm starts from a point *left* of its neutral center, while the left steering arm starts from a point to the right of its neutral center. The neutral center is a point located straight back from the steering axis on the circle the steering arm describes as it turns. If the steering arms started from their neutral centers, they would be parallel when the wheels pointed straight ahead. They would describe identical arcs and would produce identical steering angles in both wheels. Instead, the inside wheel steering arm describes a longer arc and produces a higher steering angle. Toe-out increases at a growing rate as the steering angle builds up.

This is what is known as Ackermann steering. It is quite valid at very low speeds, but is a complete fallacy at high speeds since it does not take tire slip angles into account. Yet all auto makers continue to provide Ackermann steering in order to minimize tire scrub in parking and other low-speed maneuvers with high steering angles.

The Steering Linkage
The steering system consists of a steering wheel and a steering shaft, a steering gear and a steering linkage. The steering wheel turns the

steering shaft. The steering gear changes the rotating motion of the steering shaft into a sideways motion that operates the steering linkage. Both front wheels are connected to the steering gear via a parallelogram linkage. The most common linkage consists of a pitman arm, a center link, an idler arm, and two tie rods. The steering arms are integral with the front wheel spindles and spindle support arms.

The spindle support arm is a high-tensile steel forging that holds the wheel to the chassis. The steering knuckle forms part of both suspension and steering systems. It has two ball joints—one upper and one lower. They work as hinge points for the suspension system and as swivel points for the steering system. The line between the two ball joints is called *steering axis*. The spindle support arm has a third extension called a *steering arm*. The steering arm extends backwards and dictates the steering angle.

The free end of the steering arm is attached to a tie rod by a ball joint. To keep these joints from rattling under widely changing conditions, the balls are usually spring-loaded in their sockets. The tie rod is a short bar placed transversely in the chassis, to pull on the steering arm. It moves in two planes. The whole rod moves back and forth with the linkage, and the tie rod end moves up and down with the wheel. The tie rod end can be adjusted for length. The inner end of the tie rod is connected to the center link. This is another transverse rod. It is connected to the pitman arm on one end and to the idler arm on the other. The idler arm is anchored to the frame (or body shell) and provides a rigid attachment point for the steering linkage. The pitman arm is splined on the pitman arm shaft. The pitman and idler arms are always parallel to each other and move through symmetrical arcs.

When the steering wheel is turned left, the pitman arm moves to the right, pushing the center link to the right, and pulling the left tie rod to the right. The tie rod pulls the left steering arm right, which turns the wheel to the left. The right steering arm is pushed to the right, which turns that wheel left also.

There are two main types of parallelogram steering linkages—one has a solid center link located aft of the front suspension, the second has its center link located ahead of the front suspension.

The center link member of the first parallelogram linkage is made from a forged bar rather than from tubing. The end of the center link on the opposite side from the steering gear is supported by an idler arm. This idler arm takes two forms, both having a pin-and-bushing type of bearing at the attachment between the idler arm and the bracket. One variation has a ball joint of limited angularity at the connection between the center link and the idler arm; the other variation has a pin-and-bushing bearing at this point. The inner ball sockets of the tie rods are attached to bosses which are forged or cold pressed in the center link. The tie rods customarily are bent. Adjustment is effected by a turnbuckle inserted in a straight portion of each tie rod.

The center link of the second design of parallelogram linkage is located ahead of the front wheel axis. It connects the forward ends of two levers. Each lever has a pivot point midway along its length. The inner ends of the tie rods are attached to the rear end of the levers. The tie rods are also ahead of the front centerline. A drag link running fore-and-aft on the vehicle connects the pitman arm to the plane arm on the same side of the car through an inwardly projecting bellcrank arm. Both bellcrank and idler arm rotate on pivots through the frame side rails. The intermediate member of both tie

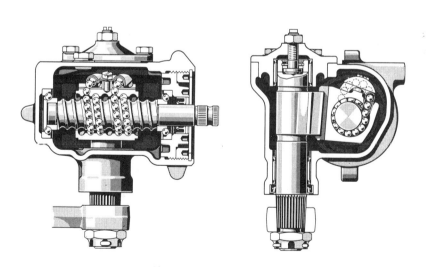

Ford parallelogram steering linkage is typical of modern practice. Idler arm is anchored to chassis frame.

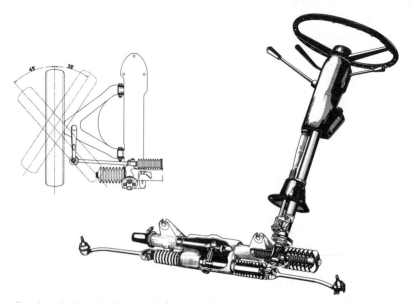

Recirculating ball steering gear has ball race on steering shaft and inside moveable rack-nut.

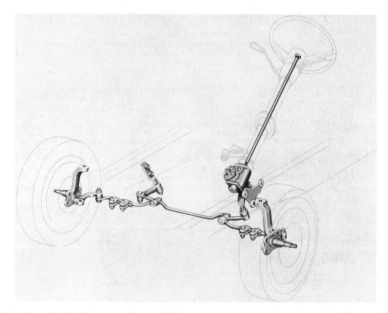

Rack and pinion steering gives extremely direct connection, and minimal risk of slack in steering linkage.

rods and center link is a threaded tube, thus providing three points of adjustment. The drag link is non-adjustable.

The Steering Gear

The task of the steering gear is to convert rotary motion from the steering wheel into linear motion in the steering linkage. The steering gear on most modern cars is the recirculating ball, worm and nut type. The worm is mounted on the lower end of the steering shaft. The ball nut rides on the worm. The worm and the nut have mating spiral grooves in which steel balls circulate to provide a low-friction drive between worm and nut.

A typical steering gear contains two sets of 25 balls. Each set operates independently of the other. The circuit through which each set of balls operates includes the grooves in worm and ball nut and a ball return guide attached to the outer surface of the nut. When the wheel and steering shaft turn to the left, the ball nut is moved downward by the balls which roll between the worm and nut. As the balls reach the outer surface of the nut they enter the return guides which direct them across and down into the ball nut, where they re-enter the circuit.

The teeth on the ball nut engage matching teeth on a sector gear forged as an integral part of the pitman arm shaft. The teeth on the ball nut are made so that a high point of tighter fit exists between the ball nut and pitman arm shaft sector when the front wheels are in a straight-ahead position. The teeth of the sector are tapered so that proper lash can be obtained by moving the pitman arm shaft endways by means of a lash adjuster screw which extends through the gear housing side cover.

The head of the lash adjuster and a selectively fitted shim fit snugly into a T-slot so that the screw also controls end play of the shaft. The screw is locked by an external lock nut. The pitman arm shaft is carried by a bushing in the steering gear housing and a bushing in the housing side cover. A seal in the housing prevents leakage of lubricant at the lower end of the shaft. The steering worm shaft is carried by two ball thrust bearings which bear against seats on the end of the worm. The outer face of the lower worm bearing is pressed into the worm bearing adjuster which screws into the housing and is locked by a nut.

This adjuster is turned to provide proper pre-loading of the upper and lower worm bearings. There are two steering adjustments on the steering gear: worm bearing preload and pitman arm shaft overcenter preload. The most important adjustment affecting steering response is the pitman arm shaft overcenter. The steering gear housing is attached to the fram (or body shell). The upper steering shaft is a separate shaft supported in the steering column jacket. Its upper and lower ends are supported in ball bearings. The upper steering shaft is connected to the steering worm shaft through a rag-type joint coupling. This coupling allows slight variations in alignment between the steering gear worm shaft and the steering shaft. If the pitman arm shaft turns one degree when the steering shaft turns 18 degrees, the *steering gear ratio* is 18 to one. A steering gear ratio of 24 to one means more work with the steering wheel to obtain a given steering angle than with the 18-to-one ratio. A higher ratio means lower effort but slower response.

The *overall steering ratio* takes the linkage into account, and gives the ratio between degrees of steering shaft rotation and degrees of steering angle. Two cars with identical steering gear can have different overall steering ratios. A longer pitman arm will give a lower overall ratio. Longer steering arms will give a higher overall ratio.

Most sports cars, and many small cars, use rack and pinion steering. It works with meshing gears, the rotational movement of the steering shaft being converted directly into linear motion by a pinion at the lower end of the shaft engaging with teeth cut in a horizontal rack which slides transversely across the car. The ends of the rack are connected to tire rods which in turn operate the steering arms. This is the most direct of all steering gears, almost totally free of lost motion but often suffering from kickback. Modern rack and pinion systems have a high helix angle on the gear teeth which effectively reduces the reversibility.

Another fairly popular type of steering gear is the worm and wheel design. The worm, fixed to the lower end of the steering column, meshes with a wheel mounted on the drop arm shaft. As the wheel is only partially rotated during movement between locks and is often replaced by a sector of a wheel. The main disadvantage is that no really satisfactory method of adjustment for wear is provided.

Various means have been devised for taking up wear between worm and wheel, but the large surface contact area between them tends to make the steering somewhat stiff in action.

Power Steering

All popular *power steering* systems are hydraulic. This does not mean that the wheels are steered by hydraulic power. The mechanical linkage is the same with power steering as with manual steering. Power steering actually means power-assisted steering. A hydraulic pump delivers power to help move the steering linkage in the direction indicated by the driver's movement of the steering wheel. When the engine is not running, or if any part of the power mechanism is inoperative, the steering gear will operate manually. This takes added effort, since the driver then has to work the power cylinder by hand.

Modern cars have *integral* power steering systems. They are called integral because the power cylinder is integral with the steering gear instead of being mounted as a separate unit. The integral power steering system is made up of a power pump driven by the engine and a power cylinder in which the piston functions as a rack meshing with a pinion sector on the pitman arm shaft.

The driver's effort on the steering wheel is always proportioned to the force necessary to turn the front wheels. When the effort on the wheel drops below a certain level pound, power assist ceases. When the steering wheel is released from a turn, the front wheels resume a straight-ahead position in the normal manner with assistance or interference from the power mechanism. For a power assisted steering gear, the nut unit with the recirculating balls is redesigned to incorporate the power cylinder piston and the rack that meshes with the pinion sector on the pitman arm shaft.

The steering shaft is a separate shaft supported in the steering column jacket. It is connected to the power steering gear through a flexible coupling which is bolted to the steering shaft flange. This flexible coupling helps absorb minor shocks and vibrations, and dampens out hydraulic noises and vibrations in the gear assembly and the steering column jacket assembly. The power steering pump is mounted on the engine in position to be driven by a belt from a crankshaft pulley. It converts some engine power into oil pressure which is used against the rack-piston nut unit to rotate the pitman arm shaft.

Power steering has no direct influence on ride and handling, but can make a sizeable contribution toward better vehicle control by enabling the driver to undertake maneuvers that would require superhuman physical strength. As a general rule, all cars with V-8 engines should be equipped with power steering for *safety reasons*.

TIRES

The Importance of Tires

While there isn't much you can do about the weight distribution or roll centers on your car, you can change the tires. Only a minority of cars are delivered with the best possible tires as original equipment. If you are buying a new car, you may want to specify your own brand and type of tire. Perhaps the standard tire size doesn't even suit you. You have a lot of options when you're buying tires, and the more you know about them the easier it will be.

The importance of tires for ride and handling cannot be overestimated. Everything depends on the tires, because they are the only form of contact between the car and the roadway: four contact patches, or footprints. These footprints have the final say in everything you want your car to do—speed up or slow down, and above all, turn. And turn with precision, not too much, and not too little.

Why should the tires make such a difference? First, remember that it's the tires that steer your car. You turn the wheel, but that doesn't make the car turn. Your steering command goes via the steering gear and linkage to the tire, and that's where the action is. All steering functions are directed to just one place; the front tire footprints. Car controllability is only as good as the footprint's contact with the roadway. Look at it this way:

When you turn the wheel, you are changing something in the front tire footprints. The first thing you change is the way the wheels point. So, you say, the tires will roll in the new direction. Not

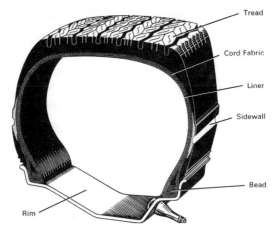

The most important part in a tire is in the middle: Air. Air carries the load, and proper inflation pressure is the first rule of both tire care and chassis tuning.

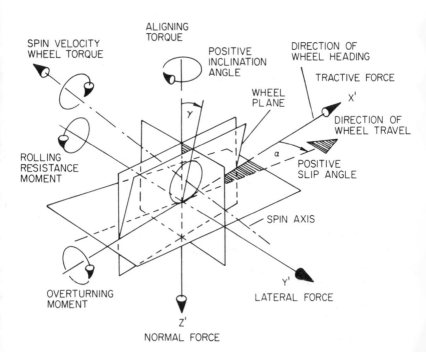

Coordinate system for forces acting on the tire show the immense complexity of the tire's duties.

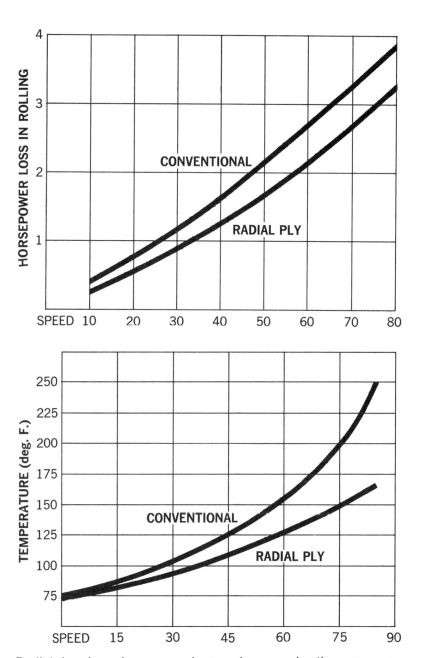

Radial tires have less power loss and run cooler than conventional tires.

quite. The tires will flex, because turning the wheels puts a side force on them. The tires don't roll exactly where they are pointed but follow a course between the straight-ahead line and the steering angle. The difference between the line the wheels are pointed on and the line they actually travel, is called slip angle.

Perhaps this is best understood if you think of the tires as a boat crossing a river. The boat points straight across but is carried downstream by the current and reaches the opposite bank some distance away from the point it was aimed at, without ever changing its course. The stronger the current, the greater the drift angle. The tire slip angle depends on vertical load, side force, coefficient of friction, and inflation pressure. Slip angle is really a misnomer. Creep angle would be a better word, for there is no slipping, sliding or skidding.

The slip angle generates a *cornering force* (side bite) in each tire. This cornering force works against the side force and is directed at right angles to the horizontal axis of the tire. What it really all boils down to is that it is the cornering force in the tires that enables a car to make turns.

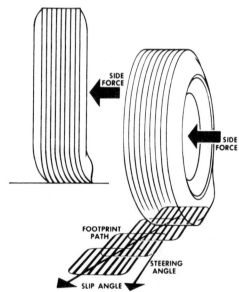

Slip angle causes sideways drift without any actual slip or skidding as a result of flexing in the tire structure.

The wheels on a parked car, or a car at speed in a straight line, are practically vertical. But under a side force, such as on a curve, the wheels do not remain upright but are tilted. The body leans because of the side force, and this sets up deflections in the suspension. How much the wheels tilt depend on the suspension geometry. This tilt is called camber, and is vitally important to the tire. That's because a tire tends to steer in the direction it's leaning to. Think of a bicycle. To turn, you don't put much of a steering angle on the front wheel, you just lean the whole bike to the side you want to go. Airplanes steer the same way—they bank on turns.

But the automobile is quite different. It does not bank, unless the roadway is banked. But it leans, you say. Sure, but it leans the wrong way. It leans or rolls in the direction of the side force—out from the turn center instead of towards it. It is important to keep the wheels from tilting too much. Extreme camber angles means that one side of the thread begins to lift, thus reducing the size of the footprint. If that happens, there is less adhesion between tire and road, and therefore reduced side bite. For best handling precision, you want maximum side bite. You can maximize sidebite by increasing tire inflation pressure to the maximum recommended.

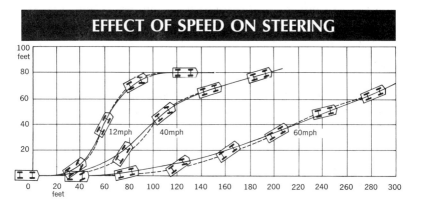

Same car, same steering wheel input, but different speeds and highly different paths.

Of course, all that air in the tire will make the tire harder. And a harder tire means a harder ride. If your car has a well-cushioned ride at normal tire pressure, you may find some harshness at maximum pressure.

Just as the tire is part of the steering system, it is also part of the springing. The tire helps soak up road surface irregularities of all kinds. Ride and handling are inseparable, whether we are talking about the entire vehicle or just the tires. It seems simple enough. More air improves handling but ruins the ride. It's true to a certain extent. But fortunately ride and handling are not incompatible. Before we go deeper into the functions of the tire, we should remind ourselves that a tire is not a simple part but a complex assembly. It has four main components: 1. the tread, which rolls on the roadway. 2. The beads, which hold the tire to the rim. 3. The carcass, which forms a casing and unites the tread and the beads. 4. Air, which supports the load. Which component is most important? The fourth: air. The tire is really just an envelope for the compressed air.

It's inflation pressure that determines the maximum load and speed capacity of a tire. Carcass strength is dictated by design load and required inflation pressure. The carcass really has nothing else to do but keep the tire together without causing any trouble of its own. Variations in tire construction have an enormous influence on the finished tire's performance characteristics. And the room for variations ranges from detail alterations to a complete change of basic concept. The best way to get a proper perspective on tire construction is to start with the performance characteristics.

Tire Properties
The tire makers try to arrive at the best combination of road adhesion and tread wear, rolling resistance and endurance, cornering force and cushioning ability, speed capacity and load limit, noise suppression and self-aligning torque.

Adhesion is a term which covers both traction and sidebite and is mainly dependent on three factors: tread pattern, footprint area, and rubber compound.

Tread wear goals often conflict with adhesion objectives because the best "cling" rubbers have the shortest tread life. Tread wear has four major causes:

1. excessive lateral distortion of the tread under cornering conditions,

2. excessive slip duration and slip velocity under cornering conditions,

3. contraction of the contact patch when rolling under normal design load, and

4. abrasion of the tread rubber compound by accelerative, braking, or cornering loads.

Rolling resistance is partly a function of friction between tire and roadway, partly a function of friction within the tire. The latter is the least obvious but by far the more important. Under normal conditions, the tread is only in rolling contact with the roadway, without rubbing friction. But inside the tire, as it flexes, there is rubbing friction, and this steals power from the car and converts it into heat that can be harmful to the tires. Tires should have the lowest possible rolling resistance.

Endurance as distinct from tread wear is mainly a reflection of the fatigue resistance of the materials used in the tire. Disregard damage caused by outside forces, and you will find that endurance failures are extremely rare. Newer and stronger materials have been introduced incessantly since the 1940s and progress is still being made. Very few tires today use natural rubber or other vegetable matters at all, as the original ingredients of automobile tires have gradually been replaced by synthetic products.

Cornering force is dependent on a number of factors outside the tire itself, but among the tire properties which influence cornering force, tread rigidity is the most important. Cornering force can be plotted as a direct function of slip angles against lateral loads.

Cushioning ability is mainly a criterion of ride comfort and increases with large tire sections and low inflation pressures. There are other factors in tire construction which affect comfort, such as the transmission of road noise and vibration, but these are also connected with the choice of construction materials as well as with design.

Speed capacity is the maximum safe speed of the tire under its normal design load. Tread rigidity and inextensibility are necessary for very high speeds. Tires run above their speed capacity will develop a hysteresis loop or standing wave in the tread behind the contact patch. Prolonged running under such conditions will lead to disintegration of the tire.

Load limit is mainly a function of sidewall strength and inflation pressure. A given air pressure is needed to support a certain load, and if the tire can't contain air at that pressure, it has a lower load limit.

Noise suppression depends on the choice of materials for the various components in a tire, tread pattern, and type of construction.

Self-aligning torque is a torque generated in the revolving wheel. It tends to make the wheel travel straight and therefore tends to straighten out the car. It is valuable to the driver, because it gives a measure of the force required to steer the car, but engineers try to avoid going to excess, as very high self-aligning torque tends to make power steering a necessity. Stiff tires have lower self-aligning torques than more flexible tires, and a light wheel has a lower self-aligning torque than a heavy wheel. Self-aligning torque increases as the slip angle builds up, until it reaches a peak and then falls off. When that happens, the slip angle will increase sharply until it becomes a skid. When self-aligning torque is lost, directional control is lost.

As the car starts into a curve, the tire deforms and lateral forces begin to act on the footprint due to the friction between tire and road. These forces vary along the full length of the footprint.

At the extreme front the rubber has only just been put down on the road and it therefore takes little or nothing of the lateral load. At the rear edge, the maximum distortion of the carcass has been reached and that's where the maximum side force is acting. In between the lateral loading varies in an almost linear pattern so that the center of the total force acts well behind the center of the footprint—the distance between the two is often called "pneumatic trail" by analogy with geometrical trail. Self-aligning torque is a product of the cornering force and the pneumatic trail.

The pneumatic trail is a key factor in what sports car drivers call road feel. The pneumatic trail is, of course, variable according to conditions. At low slip angles pneumatic trail reaches well to the rear of the footprint. As the slip angle is increased, the tread elements at the rear of the footprint are the first to reach their deformation limit. With a further increase in slip angle, the pneumatic trail is shortened. At extreme slip angles the tread elements to the rear actually loosen their grip and retreat toward neutral position before unloading, making for a negative pneumatic trail (with the effective point of side force application located *ahead* of the footprint center).

Those are the tire properties the tire engineer is concerned with. For the vehicle systems engineer in charge of selecting the original-equipment tire for a new model, the picture is somewhat different, and closer to your lines of thought as an individual customer.

Tire size is usually decided on the basis of vehicle weight, and testing will fix the acceptable load deflection line. This in turn determines the required inflation pressure. Type of tire construction is decided arbitrarily (or based on commercial considerations such as price, supply situation, or other).

The tire's resistance to ply separation is measured in actual tests. Further tests determine the tire's behavior in S-bends and its anti-skid properties on wet and dry surfaces. Tread wear has to be established on superhighways, country roads, and in city use. Limits must be set for eccentricity and flatspotting. A limit is set for radial runout to avoid overheating. Rolling resistance, noise level and side bite are measured in sull-scale tests. Further measurements include the effect of side winds. Braking distance is tested on dry and wet surfaces. Special water bath tests are made to establish the tire's aquaplaning tendency. There is also a plunger penetration test for basic structural strength and a bead unseating test comprising both braking and cornering.

The True Life of a Tire

One of the inevitable facts about the true life of a tire is that it is permanently exposed to the elements. Other parts that play vital roles in controlling the vehicle are encased and well protected. You don't see any open gears, for instance. And everything that goes into the engine is thoroughly filtered. But the tires, by the very nature of their functions, cannot be sealed away. They have to be out there, without any protection at all, exposed to all kinds of hazards.

First, the road hazards. Road hazards are nails, bottle caps, broken glass, and all manner of objects left in the path of the tire. The tire is also subject to such hazards as misalignment, overload, under-inflation, overinflation, and general neglect. The tire cannot even be shielded from sunlight, rain, or cold weather. Just being in the atmosphere ages the materials that make up the tire. And in wet weather, tires run a highly magnified risk of getting cut. Take a pen knife and try to cut a dry tire. Very difficult. Now try it with a wet tire. Almost like slicing cheese.

The true life of a tire has very high temperature variations. Not only does the ambient temperature change around the year, but the tire heats up when it works. All forces acting on the car are distributed to the tires, and the tires flex as the car runs down the road, around curves, slowing down and accelerating. Flexing causes internal friction, and this generates heat. And that's not all.

Normal road hazards do not include drivers who hit the curb with their tires when trying to park. That's an additional risk. And since power steering became common, many people make lock-to-lock turns with the car at standstill. This "static scrub" is harmful to the tread of the loaded tire. The true life of a tire is a tough existence. You might think drivers would develop a forgiving and compassionate attitude towards their tires, but that's not the case. Their demands, on the contrary, are ever-increasing.

The tire must not skid or lose its bite. The limits, naturally, depend on the surface. Drivers do not expect the same kind of traction or side bite on ice or rain-slick asphalt, in mud and snow, on sand and gravel, as they do on dry abrasive concrete, and the tire must not wear out. Many people expect tires to last for years, practically without maintenance. Tires must not blow out or go flat. They must not chunk or throw their treads, no matter what the speed. And they must not unseat at the bead, no matter how sharp the corner. Nor must they squeal or chirp on hard turns. They must not set up virbrations or give rise to harshness.

Maybe it's a good thing you can't see your front tires when you throw your car into a curve. The footprint squirms and rubs sideways against the roadway, the sidewalls flex and twist and bulge. The outside shoulder buckles under, and the inside part of the tread begins to lift. There is distortion everywhere in the tire.

The true life of a tire is not easy, even in light-duty service. To find out what kind of tires you want, you should start with the driving conditions they will live in, and find tires that can take it.

Tire Size

Tires have been growing wider (fatter) in recent years, while the rolling radius has continued to reduce. A short rolling radius has the disadvantage of making more revolutions per mile—this tends to drive tire temperature up and cause greater wear. It also makes the tire rise at a faster rate on bumps and deflect more over potholes (it goes in deeper). That means a clear ride comfort penalty for tires with short rolling radius.

Yet the rolling radius keeps getting smaller. Why? Large-diameter tires mean added unsprung weight, which is detrimental to handling precision. But above all, large-diameter tires take up more space in the "package" and space utilization and styling requirements usually get priority.

To make up for the small rolling radius, tires have been getting wider, and footprint areas have in fact been growing. If you think you want wider tires on your car, you should first consider a) what they will do for ride and handling, and b) feasibility.

Let's try to cut through some of the fog that surrounds this whole question. We'll attack it head-on, literally. Look at a tire head-on, cut-away. You are only interested in two dimensions: maximum tire width (sidewall to sidewall), and tire height (footprint to bead). Compare then, and you'll find that most tires belong in one of these three groups 1) height is 78 percent of width, 2) height is 70 percent of width, 3) height is 60 percent of width. From now on, we'll talk about 78 series, 70 series, and 60 series tires, no matter how big or small they are in rolling radius as long as they have aspect ratios of 78, 70 or 60.

Most of today's cars have 78 series tires as standard. Sporty cars usually have 70 series. They give a wider footprint and better sidewall stability. Competition-type sports cars use 60 series tires—the footprint is still wider, and the sidewalls less flexible. Any conclusions? Yes. The wider the footprint, the lower the slip angle. But there's more: with lower, stiffer sidewalls, there's a loss in cushioning ability. If you have 78 series tires, you may want 70s, but not

BELTED BIAS TIRE

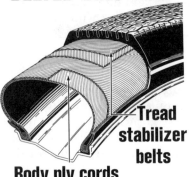

Tread stabilizer belts

Body ply cords run at bias angle

CONVENTIONAL TIRE (2 or 4 plies)

Body ply cords run at bias angle

RADIAL PLY TIRE

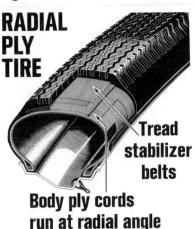

Tread stabilizer belts

Body ply cords run at radial angle

60s. If you're dissatisfied with your 70s, you may still not want 60 series tires.

You may find a 70 or a 78 tire that will fill your ride and handling requirements. That is possible because of differences in materials and types of construction.

Tire Construction

There are three basically different types of tire construction:
1. Bias-ply tires.
2. Bias/belted tires.
3. Radial tires.

Now, what are the differences that are hiding behind that terminology? Bias-ply refers to the angle of the carcass cord plies being biased in relation to the tire base line. The cord plies criss-cross at a biased angle, all around the carcass. The principle is the same whether you are talking about a two-ply tire or a four-ply tire or a six-ply tire. Most makers of bias-ply tires use rayon cord, while some use nylon and others polyester. From the consumer's viewpoint, none of these materials has any clear advantage over another.

Bias/belted indicates a bias-ply tires with the addition of a belt. The belt is placed under the tread to act as a stiffener. Belt materials are rayon, fiberglass, or steel. Rayon is the softest, fiberglass the most brittle, and steel the most resilient. Yet it is fiberglass that dominates the bias/belted tire field (with polyester carcass plies). Bias/belted tires usually have two carcass plies and two belt plies. Radial tires are also belted, but differ in the basic cord plies in that they run radially around the carcass from bead to bead, without criss-cross-

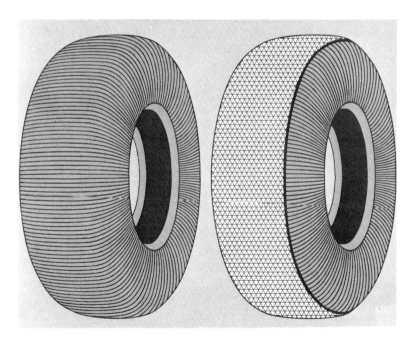

Cord plies in a radial tire run radially. Cross-hatch pattern at right represents the steel belt.

ing. Practically all radials have rayon cords. Some also have rayon belts, but all major tire makers now also offer steel-belted radials. All rayon radials usually have two carcass plies and four belt plies, while steel-belted radials usually have two carcass plies and two belt plies.

Which is best? From tire makers' test reports, SAE papers, and my own experience, I have made up the following comparison table. The ratings are based on a level of 100 for the 78 aspect ratio bias ply tire. (2-ply).

	70 Bias/Belted (fiberglass)	All Rayon Radial	Steel-belted Radial
Tread life	150	180	200
Directional stability	110	125	140
noise suppression	100	100+	100+
low-speed ride	90	90	85
high-speed ride	100	125	125
Speed capacity	125	140	140
High-speed Handling	110	125	140
Parking ease	90	85	80
Squeal suppression	120	150	180
Wet traction	110	125	125
Fuel economy	105	110	115

The steel-belted radial scored consistently highest, except in two departments: parking ease and low-speed ride. It is time to examine the steel belt and the radial carcass for an explanation of its superior dynamic behavior.

The belt braces the tread. It flexes but it's extensible. That assures extra tread life, resistance to road hazards, and lower rolling resistance. To fully explain this it is necessary to look at the footprint of the tire as the car rolls along.

Let's begin with a conventional tire. The tread pattern usually has a combination of lateral and longitudinal grooves. It's the longitudinal ones that are important in this connection. As the weight of the car flattens the tire footprint against the road surface, the tire squirms. There is a contraction in the longitudinal grooves. That gives rise to a sliding or rubbing friction between the tread and the road surface, which translates directly into tread wear. The belt of the radial-ply tire prevents tire squirm. The grooves maintain their full width, and rubbing friction is eliminated. Result: reduced tread wear and rolling resistance, improved road adhesion. This means better traction. In addition, the absence of squirm means greatly reduced risk of groove cracking. With a steel belt, road hazards cannot penetrate the tread and reach the air chamber.

Look at what happens to the sidewalls of the tire as the footprint flattens out. They bulge. This is true of both conventional and radial-ply tires. Radials bulge a lot more. But there's a big difference in what the bulging does to the tire. In the conventional tire, the bulge causes friction between the plies—because they criss-cross. This internal friction generates heat, and heat is the number one cause of tire failure (other than road hazards). In the radial-ply tire, the cord plies do not cross each other and are free to flex without fighting each other.

There is no internal friction, and the tire runs cooler. Because of this, manufacturers specify lower inflation pressures for radial-ply tire, which improves the cushioning ability of the tire, without any

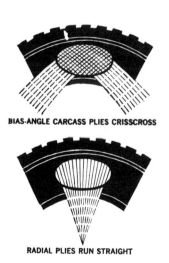

BIAS-ANGLE CARCASS PLIES CRISSCROSS

RADIAL PLIES RUN STRAIGHT

Radial tires have reduced internal friction because cords do not cross and therefore do not fight.

detrimental effect on the tire structure. Reducing inflation pressure to the same level in conventional tires would, of course, also provide better cushioning—only at the cost of a great increase in internal friction and the risk of overheating.

Because of its low rolling resistance, the radial-ply tire offers reduced fuel consumption. Because of the low heat buildup, the radial tire has higher speed capacity. It will not suffer ply separation or tread separation at speeds where a conventional tire of the same dimension and load rating would fail. Correspondingly, it will run longer without failure at a given speed, even within the speed range of the comparable conventional tire.

In a steel-belted radial, it makes no difference to the flattening of the footprint whether the car is going straight down the road or taking a curve. The flattening is caused by the weight of the car—a vertical down-force. But the curve introduces a side force on the tire, and that can cause partial lifting of the tread. The partial tread lifting in the tire can occur even in the most heavily loaded wheel (usually the outside front) and on cars with extensive wheel travel and soft springs. It can occur with conventional tires, that is, not with radials.

Here's what happens with bias-ply tires: The side force pushes against the wheel hub, and the wheel tries to move sideways. Friction between the tire and the roadway prevents sideways motion. But the force doesn't go away. As long as the tread holds its grip, the tire must absorb the side force. It is distributed evenly throughout the tire's cross section in the whole area around the footprint—and beyond. The whole tire is twisted. The cross section is deformed. One shoulder buckles under, and the opposite shoulder is lifted. It lifts part of the tread with it. That immediately cuts down the size of the footprint, which in turn reduces friction, and the tire's ability to grip. Its side bite is severely reduced. Radial-ply tires act quite differently, since the functions of the tread are completely separated from those of the sidewalls. The conventional tire acts as a unit, but in the radial tire each component has its own job.

What happens when a side load is placed on a car with radial-ply tires? First of all, the sidewalls are so flexible that the wheel is permitted some sideways motion relative to the tire. The wheel is displaced, in parallel, in the direction of the side force. There are further important differences. The stiff belt resists twisting in the plane of the wheel. Because of the belt, the side force is not evenly distributed through the tire cross section in the footprint area.

The side walls take it all, and flex freely. That is what allows the wheel its parallel sideways movement. The belt also helps keep the full width of the tread flat on the road surface, and the sidewalls aid towards this goal by keeping the flexing confined to their own area. The sidewalls distort without lifting the inside shoulder, and the outside shoulder does not buckle under.

The full footprint remains on the active list throughout the maneuver, and maximum sidebite is maintained. This translates directly into an ability to sustain higher side forces (higher cornering speeds) with greater handling precision and a higher degree of safety. In technical terms, the radial-ply tire is capable of generating higher cornering power for a given slip angle. Radial-ply tires run with low slip angles because the belt resists twisting of the tire in its longitudinal plane. Slip angle can be defined as the amount of twist in the tire tread, relative to the wheel it is mounted on. In practice this means quicker steering gain, with less understeer. The tire responds more quickly to steering inputs because a minor slip angle is enough to generate a substantial cornering force. Correspondingly, because tire distortion is spread out over the entire sidewall area and isolated from the tread, the radial tire has reduced tendency to squeal on turns, even in the later stages of its tread life.

Bias-ply tires tend to "nibble", which means that the tire makes a series of quick but minuscule directional reversals when running on or near a ridge, such as a tar strip between two lanes on a concrete highway or a road shoulder.

In such conditions the radial-ply tire does not react at all. The belt keeps it free from wander. It has higher directional stability than the conventional tire. This fact also shows up in acceleration and braking. Because of the radial tire's reduced interaction between tractive force and lateral force, directional changes during speed variations (with their attendant changes in weight distribution) are minimized.

One reputed disadvantage of radial ply tires is that even though

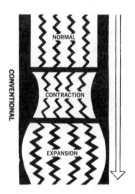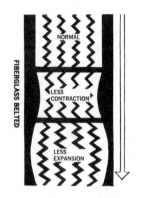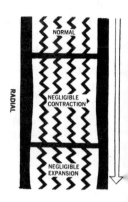

Footprint area squirms more or less depending on type of tire construction. Squirm or contraction causes high tread wear and partial loss of traction.

they will powerfully "hug" a curve in the road, they are supposed to "break away" or "let go" *without warning* when they finally reach the limit of adhesion. This is only true of certain types. Break away characteristics depend very much on the actual belt design and material used. The self-aligning torque curve (which reflects break away) of some radial tires is just as gradual as for conventional tires.

Perhaps the least understood feature of the radial-ply tire is its noise suppression characteristics. Tests have proved that it offers a substantial reduction in road roar frequencies of 100 to 300 cycles per second on noise-exciting surfaces. Yet its major drawback in the eyes of most Detroit engineers is its low-speed harshness. Don't confuse harshness with ride comfort. The radial-ply tires is softer and offers better cushioning because its cords are stressed in pure bending, while the overlapping cords in the bias-ply tire are stressed in shear. Harshness is more of a noise problem than a matter of ride comfort.

Tire resonances occur in two planes, vertical and longitudinal. This applies to both bias-ply and radial-ply tires. Bias-ply tires have their natural resonances between 150 and 250 cycles per second, while radial-ply tires have their natural resonances at far lower frequencies. The vertical resonance level of the radial-ply tires lies around 80 cycles per second, and the longitudinal resonance at around 40. This works in favor of the radial-ply tire as far as noise, vibration, and harshness are concerned. But there's more to it than that. Remember those extremely flexible sidewalls that are so essential to the handling characteristics of the radial tire? Because they are so flexible, the tire is allowed to vibrate more. Frequency may well be lower, but amplitude is far higher than for conventional tires. In addition, the rise to maximum amplitude is much sharper in the radial tire. It is quite gradual in conventional tires. The result is that the radial ply tire tends to rumble on cobblestone surfaces at low speeds. When hitting a small cobble, the tire vibrates like a drum. The shock wave is absorbed by the cord plies and dissipated as heat. With radial plies there is no such infighting, and the vibrations have free play.

Radial tires are generally recognized as offering superior wet trac-

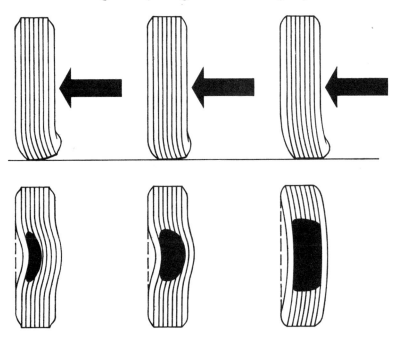

Bias-ply tire (left) rolls over on one shoulder and lifts more than half its normal footprint under high side force. Bias belted tire (center) keeps more of its footprint area on the ground due to stabilizing effect of the belt. Radial tire (right) maintains full footprint due to sidewall flexibility and belt stability.

TIRE SIZE OR DESIGNATION

| Conventional Bias Ply | | | | | Other | |
1965-On	Replaces Pre-1965	Bias and Belted Bias Ply "78 Series"	"70 Series"	"60 Series"	Radial Ply "80 Series"	"70 Series"
6.00-13					165 R 13	
		A78-13				
6.50-13		B78-13			175 R 13	
		C78-13				
7.00-13					185 R 13	
			D70-13			
					195 R 13	
6.45-14					155 R 14 165 R 14	
		B78-14				
	6.00-14					
6.95-14					175 R 14	
		C78-14				
	6.50-14					
		D78-14	D70-14			DR 70-14
7.35-14					185 R 14	
	7.00-14					
		E78-14	E70-14			ER 70-14
7.75-14					195 R 14	
	7.50-14					
		F78-14	F70-14			FR 70-14
8.25-14					205 R 14	
	8.00-14					
		G78-14	G70-14			GR 70-14
8.55-14					215 R 14	
	8.50-14					
		H78-14	H70-14			HR 70-14
8.85-14	9.00-14				225 R 14	
		J78-14	J70-14			JR 70-14
	9.50-14					
						LR 70-14
G77-14						
	6.00-15				165 R 15	
6.85-15			C70-15		175 R 15	CR 70-15
		C78-15				
	6.50-15					
		D78-15	D70-15			DR 70-15
7.35-15					185 R 15	
		E78-15	E70-15	E60-15		ER 70-15
7.75-15					195 R 15	
	6.70-15					
		F78-15	F70-15	F60-15		FR 70-15
8.15-15					205 R 15	
	7.10-15					
		G78-15	G70-15	G60-15		GR 70-15
8.25-15						
8.45-15					215 R 15	
	7.60-15					
		H78-15	H70-15			HR 70-15
8.55-15						
8.85-15					225 R 15	
	8.00-15					
		J78-15	J70-15			JR 70-15
9.00-15						
	8.20-15					
			K70-15			KR 70-15
9.15-15					235 R 15	
		L78-15	L70-15			LR 70-15
8.90-15						
6.00-16						
6.50-16						
7.00-15						
7.00-16						

tion. This is mostly as a result of their lack of footprint contraction, but that is only one side of the wet traction picture. Tire construction is in fact only one of three variable tire factors, that determine overall wet traction. The others are tread design and tread compound.

The basic principle of tread design for improved wet traction is drainage or water evacuation. Skids are caused by water separating the tire from the roadway, so it will obviously be a help if the water can be removed. The vertical load on the tire tends to push it away, but water moves best in open channels. That's why it's important to have a number of grooves—more of them the wider the tire—and to keep them open throughout the footprint area.

Lengthwise grooves allow water to escape behind the footprint, but that's not enough in most conditions. Water must also be led across the tread into the grooves, or across the shoulder ribs and out

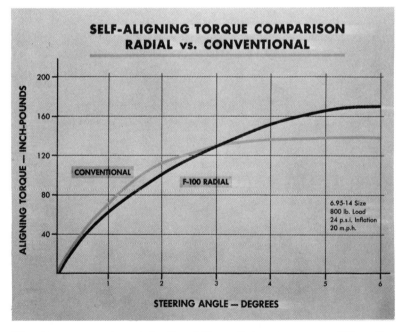

Firestone proved superiority of its radials years ago. Other tire makers claim even greater margins.

from the shoulder. On most tires this is achieved partially by a zigzag groove design and partially by siping (sipes are narrow grooves). Next, the rubber compound. As I have explained earlier, the term rubber refers to any number of synthetic materials such as polymers plus traditional ingredients such as carbon black and oil. Rubber can be applied to a tire carcass so that each area is covered by the kind of rubber that is best for the functions of that area. For instance, the sidewalls need a tougher compound than the tread.

And exactly what the tread needs is controversial. Certain tire manufacturers have developed tires with high-hysteresis or "cling" rub-

B. F. Goodrich is firmly committed to the radial tire and offers a range of radials for a variety of applications. Left to right: 60-series T A, GT-100, Steel Belt Radial, and Lifesaver Radial.

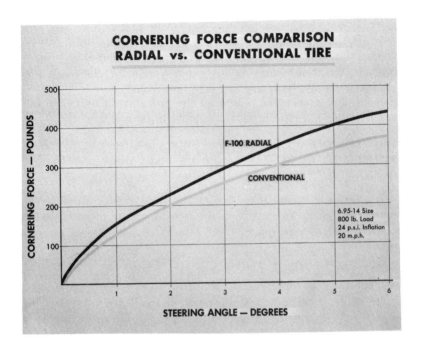

**CORNERING FORCE COMPARISON
RADIAL vs. CONVENTIONAL TIRE**

F-100 RADIAL

CONVENTIONAL

6.95-14 Size
800 lb. Load
24 p.s.i. Inflation
20 m.p.h.

CORNERING FORCE — POUNDS

STEERING ANGLE — DEGREES

Firestone's radial tire develops greater cornering force throughout the speed range, with growing advantage as speeds go up.

ber compounds that give superior wet traction. Unfortunately, the
compounds that adhere best to wet pavement are also the compounds that wear out fastest on dry surfaces. Butyl, for instance, is
a high-hysteresis ingredient that can substantially improve wet
traction, but only at the penalty of shorter tread life.

Unfortunately, the type of rubber compounds are not listed on the
tire. But you can find out about the other materials and the types
of tire construction. Sometimes the materials are identified on the
sidewall. If not, you can still find out—from a specialist publica-
tion (Tire Guide, 2119 Route 110, Farmingdale, N.Y. 11735, $3.00
per copy). All passenger car tires sold in the U.S. are listed.

Racing Car Tires

If racing cars go faster and corner at higher speeds than sports cars,
you might think you could improve your car's handling by fitting

racing tires. That's a fallacy. OK, you know that drag slicks and Indy tires without tread patterns are unacceptable for road use. Such tires have no drainage for water and easily suffer total loss of traction. In addition, their extreme width makes for very light unit loads, i.e., the weight that rests on each square inch of footprint. The lower the unit load, the lower the traction.

But surely there are other racing tires that could give your car better roadholding? Tires used in professional sports car races, for instance. The answer is no. Stay away from any tire that's designed specifically for racing. There are many and I think you'll agree, persuasive reasons for this.

Racing cars use racing tires, but racing tires are not suitable for general use. Some elements of racing tire design are proving useful in modern high-performance tires, but actual racing tires are not suitable for general use.

Why? Racing tires have no sidewall protection. This means sidewall scuffing against curbs, and also weathering protection. Racing tires are designed without any consideration for ride or noise. Tread wear is also a secondary consideration in racing tires, while it's a main quality in passenger car tires. Highspeed durability is very important in a racing tire, means that tire must withstand heat generated at speeds in excess of 200 mph. A passenger car tire never encounters those conditions. Racing tires are designed for much higher inflation pressures and require very special wide-rim wheels. Low cord angle of the racing tire gives harshness. If you could fit racing tires on your car, you would end up with: short tread life, poor wet traction, poor ride and high road noise.

Pirelli Cinturato CN-72 has rayon cords and rayon belts, and a speed capacity rating of 150 mph.

On the other hand, there are certain all-purpose tires that are accepted on race tracks (Michelin and B. F. Goodrich radials, for instance). These are high-performance road tires, and possibly the best compromises available today.

Tire Care

The importance of proper tire maintenance cannot be overestimated. Two examples will amply illustrate the point:

1. The loss of traction caused by improper inflation far outweighs the difference in traction between different types of highway tires.
2. The loss of traction caused by worn treads far outweighs the difference in traction between new highway tires of different types.

Keep your tires properly inflated at all times, and replace worn tires. Under or overinflation prevents the tire tread from being flat against the road. This results in more rapid wear of certain areas of the tread, thus shortening the life of the tire. Underinflation overworks the tire, because a softer tire flexes more. This creates heat that weakens the structural cords, which could result in serious tire failure. Overinflation causes a problem by making the tire hard, preventing it from deflecting properly when striking bumps and foreign objects. This can lead to fabric breaks.

MICHELIN zX   **MICHELIN Xas**   **MICHELIN Xvr**

Recent variations on the classic Michelin X tire include the zX for low-performance cars, XAs (assymmetrical) for high-performance cars, and XVR (for very extreme performance road cars).

If you plan to drive long distances at high speeds, your tire pressure should be increased by four pounds (but not above the maximum cold inflation level). This increase in pressure reduces flexing enough to make the tire run cooler at high speeds. Do not bleed air from tires when they are hot, because the pressure is higher than normal. The pressure will drop as much as six pounds when tires cool.

Check inflation at least once a month. And check it when the tires are not hot from driving. Carry your own air gauge. Many of the automatic "air tower" gauges are off as much as 6 lbs. You should also check your tires for cuts, cracks, bruises, and bulges. A good time for this is when the car is up on a grease rack. Rocks and pieces of glass and metal should be removed from the tread at this time. They can work their way up into the tire and cause tire failure.

Overloading of tires occurs when the combined weight of the

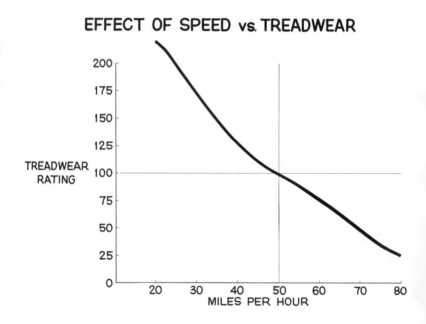

EFFECT OF SPEED vs. TREADWEAR

This chart shows how tread life is shortened by high speed driving. It's an average curve—radials are better, and bias-ply tires worse than indicated.

vehicle, its passengers, and cargo exceed the combined load rating of its tires. Overloading causes excess strain and flexing of tire sidewalls which can damage structural cords, leading to tire failure. Improper wheel alignment causes excessive tread wear on one shoulder of the tread surface. This can sometimes be seen by a feather edge which develops on one side of tread rows. It is smart to have alignment checked every 10,000 miles. But make sure it is done by a reputable, authorized shop. Unbalanced tires cause shimmy and vibration and the tread wears excessively in spots, shortening tire life. Wheel balancing takes only a few minutes and is inexpensive in relation to the extra tire life and driving pleasure gained.

Tread life is seriously shortened at higher speeds. Radials are less affected than bias-ply and bias/belted tires, but it's true of all tires that speed works against tread life.

Driving methods have more influence on tread life than any other factor (except gross neglect, of course). Henry Hodges, head of the Nevada Automotive Test Center in Carson City, has established a tread-wear index for various types of driving (lowest index number means longest tread life):

Racing	1.0
Hot-rodding	0.7
Mountain driving	0.5
City Streets	0.4
Surburban roads	0.3
Superhighways	0.2

You don't have to be a mathematical wizard to see that you can double your tread life, even in city and suburban driving (index average 0.35) if you avoid jackrabbit starts, slamming on the brakes at the last moment, and throwing your car around turns.

WHEELS

The driving wheels are designed to carry a part of the weight of the vehicle plus road shocks and driving torque. The wheels are made as light as possible to keep down unsprung weight, while being strong enough to resist local deformation. Most modern cars have five-hole stamped disc wheels made of pressed steel. The wheel is non-tapered and usable for both front and rear wheel applications. Attachment is by beveled nuts on three, four, five or more studs.

These wheels are made from two pressings, the rim and the disc member. To give added strength, the disc has convolutions both radially and laterally. Perforations in the disc portion located between the center cavity and the rim are used for ventilation, which is needed to keep the brakes cool. Hub caps cover the wheel center and often extend right out to the rim. The central part of the disc has a number of equally spaced holes, counter-sunk, for the hub attachment studs.

Wheel sizes are given in a simple code, such as 4½K-14. What does that mean? The first number 4½, is rim width in inches, measured across the tire bead seat. The second number, 14, is the wheel diameter in inches, measured from bead to bead, through the wheel hub center.

The letter has to do with rim flange height. Not all wheels have the same type of flange. Why? Because tires are too different. Different types of tires require different rim flange shapes to be kept in correct shape when inflated, and to hold them in place when cornering.

The taller the tire's aspect ratio for a given rim width, the higher the flange required for proper seating. The importance of the rim flange is readily realized when you see that it is the only contact area between the wheel and the tire. All other wheel dimensions are secondary to flange height. The tire determines the necessary flange height, and the dimensions for the rest of the wheel are by-products of the flange height. A given flange height dictates a certain well depth in the middle of the rim, so that the tire can be mounted and dismounted without damage to its beads.

Most wheels have a 5-degree slope from the well to the flange, which enables the bead to slide gradually to its seat. Some wheels have a retainer hump at the edge of the slope, nearest the well, to keep the bead from sliding off its seat and across the rim in case of sudden deflation or tire failure.

Matching the tire to the rim is no problem if you treat the question with proper deference to the tire makers' recommendations. A mis-

Standard 5-stud wheel and wheel cover.

Wheel Dimensions

Rim Code	Rim Width	Flange Height	Well Depth	Rim Diameter
3½J-13	3.5	0.687	0.75	13
3½J-14	3.5	0.687	0.75	14
3½J-15	3.5	0.687	0.75	15
4J-13	4.0	0.687	0.75	13
4J-14	4.0	0.687	0.75	14
4J-15	4.0	0.687	0.75	15
4½J-13	4.5	0.687	0.75	13
4½J-14	4.5	0.687	0.75	14
4½J-15	4.5	0.687	0.75	15
5J-13	5.0	0.68	0.70	13
5J-14	5.0	0.68	0.70	14
5J-15	5.0	0.68	0.70	15
5K-13	5.0	0.77	1.00	13
5K-14	5.0	0.77	1.00	14
5K-15	5.0	0.77	1.00	15
5K-16	5.0	0.77	1.00	16
5½J-13	5.5	0.68	0.70	13
5½J-14	5.5	0.68	0.70	14
5½J-15	5.5	0.68	0.70	15
5½K-14	5.5	0.77	1.00	14
5½K-15	5.5	0.77	1.00	15
5½K-16	5.5	0.77	1.00	16
6JK-13	6.0	0.71	0.80	13
6JK-14	6.0	0.71	0.80	14
6JK-15	6.0	0.71	0.80	15
6L-15	6.0	0.85	1.125	15
6½JK-13	6.5	0.71	0.80	13
6½JK-14	6.5	0.71	0.80	14
6½JK-15	6.5	0.71	0.80	15
6½L-15	6.5	0.85	1.125	15
6½L-16	6.5	0.85	1.125	16
7L-13	7.0	0.85	1.00	13
7L-14	7.0	0.85	1.00	14
7½L-13	7.5	0.85	1.00	13
7½1-14	7.5	0.85	1.00	14

match can cause rapid tire failure. First, you can damage the tire by fitting it on the wrong rim, before you have even covered a quarter-mile on it. The reason is the rim flange height. Forcing a tire bead over a higher rim flange than it's designed for can ruin a tire irreparably.

Wheels must be balanced—and kept in balance. The present industry standard is to balance wheels to the nearest ½ ounce. There are two kinds of balance: Static and dynamic. Static balance is balance at rest. Dynamic balance is balance in motion. A wheel that

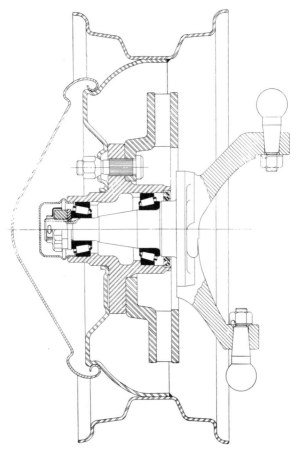

Cross section of front wheel for a typical U.S. car with tapered roller bearings.

is statically balanced can be off in dynamic balance. When the weight of a wheel assembly is equally distributed around the spindle, it is in static balance. Static imbalance makes a wheel hop up and down as it rolls along. Static imbalance is often harmonic. That means its effects may be strong at a certain speed and weaker at other speeds. Dynamic balance is an equal distribution of weight around the vertical centerline of the wheel. It usually shows up at speeds of 60 m.p.h. and higher. It makes each wheel shake rapidly one way and the other on its steering axis.

It's a basic rule of chassis tuning that the wheels be properly balanced *on the car*, which takes account of tires and brakes as well as the wheel itself. Most good service shops are equipped to do this. If you want to improve your wheel-and-tire combinations beyond simple balancing, there are several approaches open. The most common approach is to get wider tires. A little wider-than-standard tires may fit on your standard rims (follow tire makers' recommendations to the letter). For extra wide tires, you will need wider rims.

Wider rims (matched to the proper tires) will give added handling stability. Many car makers offer wider rims as a regular production option, and dealers have them in stock.

For the ultimate improvement in wheels, you can get custom wheels. There are many different types, and not all are commendable, and not all will be suitable for your car. What are the attractions of custom wheels? Above all, lightness. Lighter wheels mean reduced unsprung weight, which is important for both ride and handling. Other qualities sought in custom wheels are higher stiffness and improved resilience, truer running, and better durability.

Most custom wheels are built to closer tolerances than standard wheels. They tend to have less runout, radial and lateral, than wheels that are OKed by the car makers.

Custom wheels are usually made of light alloy (aluminum, magnesium, or elektron). Plastic wheels are still experimental but hold great promise. Wire wheels are no longer used. Some custom wheels are simply ordinary pressed steel wheels with chrome plating. These are strictly for style, and do not help your chassis tuning efforts. Another type of custom wheel is the all-steel cast wheel (styled to look like "mag" wheels). This type has no chassis-tuning advantages to offer.

Chrome-plated steel wheel is strong but heavy.

Steel-rim wheel with aluminum center is compromise solution.

Perhaps the most popular custom wheel is the type which has a standard steel rim with a magnesium or aluminum center piece. Some are welded up, others are riveted. Both types are lighter than all-steel wheels. The best custom wheels are those cast as one piece of light alloy. Elektron wheels made in Italy by Cromodora in Torino or Campagnolo in Bologna are considered the leaders in this field. Magnesium wheels of British and domestic manufacture are available from a number of sources. For literature and prices, write to:

Cromodora elektron wheel is light and looks great.

Halibrand Engineering Company
1510 West 228th Street
Torrance, California 90501

Mickey Thompson Equipment Company
Box 1770
Long Beach, California 90813

Moon Equipment Company
10820 So. Norwalk Blvd.
Santa Fe Springs, California 90670

Sears, Roebuck & Company (Different
    locations in all parts of the country).

Magnesium is one-quarter the weight of steel and two-thirds the weight of aluminum. Elektron is still lighter and stronger. Titanium and beryllium are even lighter, and have good tensile strength properties, but cost would be prohibitive.

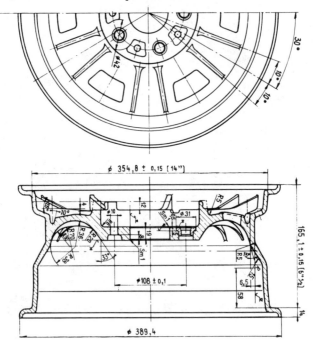

Cross section and part elevation of Cromodora elektron wheel.

Magnesium has a couple of problems you should know about. The metal can crack or even collapse unless properly alloyed, carefully cast, and heat-treated to perfection. Magnesium is also flammable. An overheated brake may not start a fire, but sparks flying from a collision certainly can. But magnesium's worst enemy maybe corrosion. Salt is extremely harmful. Minor pitting damage can in turn lead to fatigue failure. If you do want magnesium wheels, make sure they are of a reputable brand, and keep them well protected.

A switch to custom wheels often involves greater offset. Wheels with greater offset increase the track. Offset is the distance between the wheel's mounting plate and the center line of the rim. Wider track will make it more difficult to overturn the car, whether it's front or rear, or both. But widening the track at one end and not the other will affect weight transfer. Wider track = less weight transfer.

Greater wheel offset must be kept within strict limits. It causes a significant rise in bearing loads. At the front end, it can seriously upset the delicate balance of static wheel alignment. Most experts agree that offset should be kept within ⅛-inch.

Wheel bearings—on all wheels—are subjected to both radial and axial loads. On most modern cars, both front and rear hubs therefore have tapered roller bearings. Tapered roller bearings can take thrust in one direction only, so wheel bearings are usually made as an opposed pair of tapered roller races. This offeres the possibility of adjustment to take up wear.

In general, roller bearings have a higher load capacity than ball bearings, but also slightly more friction. The efficiency of the bearing depends on the preservation of a highly polished finish on the rolling elements and raceways. Should any of these surfaces become corroded or damaged by dirt or other extraneous, abrasive material, the pure rolling action will be impaired. Vibration will follow, the rolling surfaces will break up and the silent, free running accuracy of the bearing will be lost.

A completely inelastic steel roller placed between two completely inelastic steel plates will have practically no resistance to motion of one plate relative to the other. Perfectly inelastic steel rollers and surfaces cannot be produced. There is always a little deformation, which gives rise to some amount of friction. An element of sliding friction is introduced. However, this sliding friction is not influenced by bearing load. Roller bearings are lubricated to overcome the slight sliding friction, and for protection of the surfaces.

Wheel bearings are not normally designed to take shock loads, since tires and springs will absorb the shock loads under all impact loading conditions. Front wheel bearings are adjusted to allow about .002 to .004 inches and float. If disc brakes are fitted, any greater freedom than this will allow the discs to tilt on corners. The result will be that the brakes, being self-adjusting, will adjust themselves to excessive clearances. The pads will also wear unevenly, at an angle, reducing their effective area and their efficiency.